Tony B

Born in Wingates, Westhoughton. Educated at Sacred Heart Primary, Westhoughton, Thornleigh Salesian College, Bolton and De La Salle Teacher Training College, Middleton. Tony has worked as a labourer in a weaving shed and on a building site, as a bank cashier, a house father and social worker. He has been the lead singer of The Houghton Weavers folk group since 1975. He has been a Tutor of adults with Special Needs at Bolton College since 2004. Tony is married with three children who are his pride and joy.

KEEP FOLK SMILING

TONY BERRY

peakpublish

Peak Publish
An imprint of Peak Platform
New Bridge, Calver
Hope Valley
Derbyshire
S32 3XT

First published by Peak Publish 2011

A CIP catalogue record for this book is available from
the British Library

This is a work of fiction. Any resemblance to any living or
dead persons, specific cities or towns,
is purely coincidental.

ISBN: 978-1-907219-23-8
www.peakplatform.com

Acknowledgements

With special thanks to all who have helped me with this project - you know who you are.

For Teresa, Anne and James

One

Admission Free, Pay at the Door

I always knew that I was amongst the luckiest people on this planet. I realised it when, at the tender age of five-ish I found a florin, two bob, ten pence, whatever! We'd, that's me and my brother James, been to the 'duck pond' fishing with our handmade tackle (cotton, bent pin, etc.) and when we realised they weren't biting we joined them for a swim. We then went for a walk to the Iron Bridge (not the one Telford built: I'd never even heard of him); no, the one near De Havilland where my dad used to work. I'll mention my dad at this juncture because when I found the florin, two bob, ten pence, whatever, it was on my dad's birthday so without further ado I bought him a birthday present with the money, twenty Senior Service for one shilling, eleven and a half pence, leaving a halfpenny for me to buy a load of sweets!

When we were little we'd get up early and play out until it went dark and then we'd go home. We spent very little time in the house because there was nothing to do at home only play board games, cards or pray. We prayed quite a lot in those days; did that make us lucky?

I've often thought of how lucky I was from that time on; best parents, best sisters, best neighbours, best friends and best town in the whole wide world. I didn't mention my brother then 'cos we were always fighting and it wasn't until much later that I realised I'd got the best brother in the world as well!

We weren't poor - we had no money - but neither did anybody else we knew. We were all in the same boat so it didn't make a difference to us kids. A friend of mine wrote a song much later in life with some words that summed up the whole of my childhood.......''the times were hard but people always smiled, and then when times got better, no-one smiled at all......."   It probably says a lot about the world as we know it today.

We'd learn stupid rhymes from my dad like:

"I went to the pictures tomorrow
I took a front seat at the back
A kind lady gave me an apple
I ate it then gave it her back"

..............and..............

"One fine day in the middle of the night
Two dead men got up to fight
Back to back they faced each other
Drew their swords and shot each other!"

There were very few unhappy times that I can remember during my formative years. Well, I nearly cut my thumb off with a broken jam jar in the churchyard, still got the scar to prove it. Me and my mother were taking flowers to somebody's grave. We used jam jars for the flowers; I dropped the vessel and when trying to pick it up I slashed my thumb, hurt a lot, but when I think of the mother who was buried in that same churchyard then there's no comparison. She died shortly after her husband, brother and four sons were blown up and died at the Pretoria mine just down the road – now that's hurt!

The churchyard and church of St. John the Evangelist holds a lot of memories, both happy and sad. I've attended quite a few weddings there but probably twice as many funerals. Religion, the cause of so much hurt in this world has a lot to answer. I wasn't allowed to set foot in that church unless I got permission from our local parish priest; I was brought up a Catholic and the two religions sometimes had their differences!

All the trouble in Ireland was so difficult for me to understand as I was growing up. My father's mother emigrated from Northern Ireland and came to live in Wingates where she met her future husband, my granddad. She was a Roman Catholic and when she arrived in town she attended the local Catholic Church. One day, however, she had a row with the priest and vowed never to set foot in that church again. From that point onwards all her family were brought up as Church of England followers and it wasn't until my dad and future mother met and fell in love that my father started to attend the Catholic Church.

3

When they married he became a Catholic – so my dad was a Catholic and a Protestant but he got on quite well with himself!

The church I have just mentioned lies in the small hamlet of Wingates which in turn is part of the town of Westhoughton. The town has a couple of nicknames, 'Howfen' or 'Keaw Yed City' (Cow Head City). The townsfolk are very proud of their town and are known locally as Keaw Yeds. There are several reasons for this name but the general populous prefer the tale about the farmer and his cows or keaws as we'll now call them!

Once upon a time...... a farmer was bringing his herd of keaws in for milking one morning when he realised that one was missing. When he eventually found the unfortunate beast, its head was stuck in the gate at the end of the field. After pondering for some time in the hope of reaching a solution to his problem, he set off for the tool shed. He emerged from the shed with a saw in his hand and proceeded to saw off the keaw's head! When asked why he hadn't sawed the gate he proudly answered, "Now I thought about that....but then realised that the gate cost me twice as much as the keaw, so the answer was easy! I have meat for the family and my gate is still in one piece".

Several less interesting reasons are given for our love affair with cows; one being that Westhoughton had a cottage industry of silk weaving in the dim and distant past. When a bolt of silk was finished it was rolled into a long tube which the weavers would carry over their shoulders giving the impression that they had horns. Full

4

oxen were apparently roasted over an open fire to celebrate the end of the Napoleonic war in 1815 and locals formed two teams to fight over the head, which was hoisted on a pole and paraded around the streets. I would like to think that one of the opposing factions came from Wingates and that they were the inevitable winners! Finally, the most logical solution of all came from Canon Tom Davies, vicar of the Parish church. He explained that the church is named after St. Bartholomew, commonly regarded as the patron saint of butchers and tanners, whose emblem has always been a cows head. So maybe one of them is right but I, like the rest of the town, prefer the old legend!

Two

History

The town has one or two quite interesting tales to tell. During the English Civil War, a battle was fought on Warcock Hill, just off Bolton Road, in 1642, between the Roundheads and the Cavaliers who were based in Bolton and Wigan respectively. It's also believed that Prince Rupert of the Rhine gathered his troops in Westhoughton before the Massacre of Bolton on 28th May 1644.

Prince Rupert seems to be an amazingly colourful character. He was a soldier, an inventor and an artist. Historians liken him to Errol Flynn, a swashbuckling film star of the 50's. Prince Rupert must have been a fairly remarkable and bloodthirsty figure, having fought against Spain in the 80 Years War, The Holy Roman Empire in the 30 Years War and commander of the Royalist cavalry in the English Civil War, together with a few years as a buccaneer in the Caribbean. He stood six foot four inches and every time he went into battle he was accompanied by his poodle named "Boye". I can just imagine him riding past the 'White Lion' on Market Street with Boye at his side. All the blokes, with a pike staff in one hand and a tankard of ale in the other shouting, "Seems like a nice Boye!"

There was, supposedly, a sighting of Bonnie Prince Charlie whizzing his way through the town, on his flight back to Scotland, but if it was by one of those blokes outside the White Lion, it could have been anybody!

It is recorded that Iorweth and Madoc Hulton came to Westhoughton in 1167 from Wales although other writers claim their origins to be Norman. With names like Iorweth and Madoc I think I'll believe the former. Whichever is true, by the late 19th century the Hulton family estate comprised of over 1,300 acres. The most famous of the Hulton clan was probably the railway pioneer, William Hulton, who was responsible for the building of the Bolton and Leigh railway which ran through Westhoughton. Hope Cottage, on Manchester Road at Chequerbent was the original station house cum signal box for the Bolton and Leigh railway and when the railway fell into disrepair it was sold off as a dwelling. A friend of mine bought it and I remember going into the roof space, with him, to sort out some problem or other. When we'd finished we were absolutely filthy; probably from the smoke from all the many steam engines that had passed by over the years. I probably had some soot on me that belonged to "Stephenson's Rocket".

The railway was one of the first in the world and was surveyed and prepared by George Stephenson himself, together with his son, George. The first locomotive to run on the line was made by the Stephensons and was named, "The Lancashire Witch".

During the early part of the 19th Century, trouble was brewing throughout Britain as mechanisation was coming into the Weaving mills. The "Luddites", who were opposed to unskilled workers taking their jobs, began to destroy the new wide framed looms. It was eventually made a capital offence and many of these protestors were hanged or transported to Australia. In 1804 a gentleman by the name of Mr. Lockett built one of the first steam powered mills in the world opposite the White Lion (Probably on Mill Street or is that too obvious). In 1812, this very mill was torched by some protestors, in what was one of the very first major terrorist acts in this country. Twelve men were arrested by William Hulton, who was then High Sheriff of Lancashire, and four were publicly hanged outside Lancaster Castle. One of the men sentenced to death was Abraham Charleston who was reputed to be disabled and only twelve years of age. His heinous crime was to break one of the windows in the mill with his crutch. His parents protested but he was not reprieved and died on the scaffold in June of that year. Five others were transported to the penal colony of Australia.

During the research for this tale I found that criminals were also transported to America until the American Revolution in 1776. On a lighter note, I don't think you could choose whether you went to America or Australia. A friend of mine recently emigrated to Australia and during his many visits to Australia House was asked a multitude of questions. The last one was "Do you have a criminal record?" He replied "I didn't think you still needed one!" Didn't go down too well that one!

William Hulton had an even greater claim to fame or should one say, "infamy", several years later. At the age of twenty-four he was known as a man who dealt very harshly with any working man or woman who protested against the state or who wanted to form a trade union. In 1819 he was made chairman of the Lancashire and Cheshire magistrates. This was a special committee formed to deal with unrest amongst the workforce. On the 16th July 1819 Henry Hunt was due to speak about Political Reform in Manchester. The meeting took place at St. Peter's Field in the centre of Manchester. Hulton had arranged for Yeomanry to be there in case of trouble. What took place was later to be known as the Peterloo massacre, named after the recent battle at Waterloo.

Many hundreds attended the meeting and William Hulton felt that it would be wise to arrest Henry Hunt. During the ensuing hours the cavalry were despatched and 11 people were killed and over 400 injured. Hulton was later reported as saying "The 16th August 1819 was the proudest day of my life!"

The last surviving member of that family was Sir Geoffrey Hulton who I knew reasonably well through church, scouting and being a Keaw Yed. When he died in 1993 he didn't leave an heir so the title died with him after 700 years. My mother worked for the family for a few years as a cleaner and we had the most beautiful curtains in our street when Lady Hulton decided to throw them out!

9

The town has had many, many coal mines over the years but no-one in Westhoughton can mention coal mining without referring to the Pretoria Pit. On the 21st December 1910, 344 boys and men lost their lives following an explosion in the Plodder Mine of number 3 Bank Pit. It was probably caused by a build up of gas from a roof collapse the previous day. Of the 345 who went down the Plodder seam four came to the surface alive. Unfortunately, two of them died shortly afterwards and a rescuer perished. This was the worst accident (and resulted in the greatest loss of life) in a Lancashire coal field. Unfortunately, that would not be any consolation to the many hundreds who died throughout our county in what is a very, very dangerous occupation. Perhaps the worst affected family was the Tyldesley's. Miriam Tyldesley lost her husband, two brothers and her four sons in a few short moments on that December morning. Looking through the records it's interesting to know that life goes on. A young couple, about to be married at Christmas time, had to re-arrange their service to five o'clock in the morning to avoid the multitude of funerals taking place.

The life of the miner was terribly hard and whilst looking through old books and papers I came across this little snippet. *The human price for coal was high. In the 1930's a Bolton dentist complained about some 'Trencherbone cobbles' being half a crown a bag. The coalman said to him quietly, "A miner has gone down into the bowels of the earth to get that coal for thee. It's the best coal that can be bought. It's been brought up on the shaft, screened and sent in a wagon to the sidings.*

We've filled it, brought it out here, an put a full hundredweight into thy coal shed for half a crown. If you think that's too much I'll bring it out again. Last week you charged my daughter six-and-sixpence to have a tooth out and it took you less than fifteen minutes. I don't see what you have to grumble about". Britain revisited, Tom Harrison. Gollanz 1961

Before we get back to my tale there are just a few more interesting facts that I think you should know about.

In 1784, John Wesley preached at Barnaby's farm, Wingates and in Westhoughton itself, to try to convert the populace to Christianity. The stone from which he preached is now situated outside the Methodist church in Wigan Road whilst the place he preached is noted by another stone on Cricketers Way. John Wesley, although the founder of the Methodist Church, lived his life as a member of the Anglican faith and the Methodist Church left the Church of England in 1795, after his death in 1791. To show how things were slightly different in those days it's worth knowing that Wesley was the fifteenth child of Samuel Wesley and his wife Susanna Annesley, who in turn was the twenty-fifth child of Dr. Samuel Annesley and his poor wife! Now did they have so many children because the infant mortality rate was so high, or because there was nothing else to do in those days? Or, maybe they wanted their own football team?

King George V1 and Queen Elizabeth visited Westhoughton for thirty four minutes on Friday 20th May 1938 on their tour of Lancashire! All I can think of is a bloke chasing after the entourage with a stop watch timing every move! I don't think they could have seen much during their visit. Some might say there isn't a lot to see anyway! He was probably trying to keep up with Bonnie Prince Charlie!

Westhoughton has quite a few interesting tales to tell. For example, there's a Pie shop on Church Street that, amazingly, used to close for lunch (dinner to me!). It sells 'rice pies' which is a delicacy I've only ever found in this town. What's a 'rice pie' you ask ... well it's rice pudding in a sweet pastry case with currants and cinnamon on top ... absolutely gorgeous!

You'll know a 'moggie' as a cat I'm quite sure, but here in Howfen, a moggie is a mouse.

I read recently that Westhoughton has been re-named 'The Little Apple' following an attempt to have the town twinned with New York. You see we have a Central Park and a Carnegie Hall but the application was turned down. Oh, I am surprised! It reminds me of the two blokes in New York, one says to the other, "Excuse me pal, how do I get to Carnegie Hall?"

The other guy replies, "Practice son, practice!"

Three

Surrounding Areas

The town is situated midway between Bolton and Wigan. Up until the turn of the 20th century we were far more affiliated to the 'pie eaters' than the 'trotters'. The inhabitants of Wigan as I've just said are known as 'pie eaters'. Nowadays, they would say it's because of their love for pies; the town has many, many pie shops! It's believed that the real reason stems from the mining industry. During the early months of 1926, mine owners decided that they would decrease miners' wages by 13% and extend their shifts from seven to eight hours. The miners, quite understandably, didn't want this to happen and a General Strike was called. The slogan that the miners used was 'Not a penny off the pay, not a second on the day!' There were riots throughout Great Britain and everyone suffered. From May to October the miners held out but eventually they started to return to work, especially the ones with young families. By the end of November most had returned to work or been made redundant. Those that were employed were forced to accept longer hours, lower wages, and district wage agreements. Because the Wigan miners had returned to work before their counterparts in neighbouring districts, who had negotiated better conditions for their miners they were forced to eat 'humble pie', hence 'pie eaters'. Although an insult, Wiganers have taken the title to heart and are now proud of being pie eaters, so much so that the World Pie Eating Championships take place every year at Harry's bar situated in the town centre on Wallgate. I was driving through the town recently and came to some traffic light, behind a bakery van. A sign on the back door read, 'There are no pies kept in this vehicle overnight!'

One of my favourite tales to come from Wigan relates to a Mabel Norris de Haigh who was married to Sir William Bradshaw. Sir William, so the legend goes, went off to fight in the Holy Wars. Apparently, Mabel got word that her husband had died and fancied a bloke down the road! After the few weeks of wearing black she up's and marries this Welsh knight. Seven years later, Sir William returns from his Crusades trip only to find Mabel settled down with 'Taffy'. He promptly pursues him all the way to Newton-le-Willows kills him and tells Mabel that because of her infidelity, she must walk from their home in Haigh Hall to the cross on Wigan Lane, barefoot and dressed in sackcloth, once a week for the rest of her life; understanding sort of a bloke don't you think. The cross, at Standish, henceforth became known as "Mab's Cross".

Wigan is a very old town and is possibly the site of a Roman town known as Coccium. Most of the evidence points towards Standish but it's near enough for the inhabitants of the place to feel roman. Just walk the streets at weekend and you'll find many wearing togas and suchlike! Go on Boxing Day and you'll find Superman and Elvis Presley amongst the roman legions!

During the English Civil War the town was fiercely Royalist. This is probably because the Earl of Derby, leader of the king's forces in the North had made Wigan his headquarters. For this support, the king presented the town with a sword bearing the Royal coat of Arms which is still part of the towns' civic regalia to this day. In 1643, Parliamentary forces from Bolton ransacked the town and demolished its fortification. In a retaliatory attack the following year the forces from Wigan struck at Bolton . In 1648 Oliver Cromwell himself led troops into battle at Standish. The final battle of the English Civil war took place in what became known as the 'Battle of Wigan Lane'. These battles are re-enacted every year when Wigan Athletic and Bolton Wanderers meet in the Premiership. Hordes from Bolton enter the town and are given a civic reception (I don't think!) by the "Latics" fans. This is reciprocated at the Reebok on their return visit!

So, being stuck between these warring factions has made 'Keaw Yeds' wonderfully resolute. As I said earlier, most of our affiliations, up until the turn of the twentieth century, 1924 to be precise, have been towards Wigan. So what was it that brought us under the watchful eye of the Bolton "trotters"; simply the tram! In December 1924 a link from Bolton to Westhoughton was opened which made access to the town far easier than previously and affiliations began to sway towards Bolton.

Bolton's history is somewhat different than their neighbours. It began its life as Bolton-le-Moors, the title still used by the Rotary club in the town. During the Civil War it stood alone in the North West in support of Parliament. The town suffered three attacks by the Royalists led by Prince Rupert and James, the seventh Earl of Derby. The town finally fell to the Royalist forces in 1944 and suffered the only massacre of the Civil Wars. After the wars, James was tried for his part in the massacre and was beheaded on Churchgate after spending his last night at 'Ye Olde Man and Scythe' pub. He probably consumed several pints of its famous cider before climbing the gallows and most likely didn't feel a thing as he left this mortal coil!

A small town originally, it began to expand rapidly during the Industrial Revolution and is now one of the largest towns in Britain. Its Coat of Arms tells you nearly everything you need to know about its history. The crest contains an upward pointing arrow (or **bolt**) to celebrate the archers from the town who fought at the battle of Flodden in 1513. An elephant carrying a castle or stockade refers to the **ton** as the other part of the name. Two black lions represent the Flemish people who settled here in the 14th Century and established the textile industry. There's also a 'mule' spindle in honour of Samuel Crompton who was born and lived in the town. The Flemish also brought what was to become part of the 'national costume' of Lancashire; clogs! Finally, the motto, "Supera Moras" meaning 'Overcome delays' ...they'd obviously spent some time on Moor Lane, waiting for a bus!

Four

Wingates

Let's picture the scene of Wingates as a boy. There was a small community in that tiny hamlet. Two butchers, (Baxter's and the Co-op), Greengrocers called Cleworth's, next to him a Cobbler's and around the corner on the same block Doctor Leo's surgery. As a friend pointed out recently, you could get body and sole repaired in that small row!

Going back to the butchers, that's another story. When I was a lad it was owned by Joe Beazley but was called Baxter's, the previous owner. When Joe Beazley died and Mike Heald took it over it changed its name to Beazley's. So the only time that poor Mike will get his name in lights is when he pops his clogs! He still makes the best meat pies in the northern union!

Opposite the doctor's was a general store (Mrs. Oakes') and a 'herb' store which sold pop and milkshakes, not forgetting the Post office, five pubs, if you go as far as the Wagon and Horses which was probably two or three hundred yards away, the Labour Club and Band Room. The Band Room being home of Wingates Temperance Brass Band a very famous Westhoughton institution. They have won many championships over the years and are still going strong today. They are no longer 'temperant' as they got a short sponsorship from Bass Charrington, the brewing company.

I forgot about the bakery opposite and another couple of shops that sold all sorts of things, together with three co-operative shops next to the butchers that sold everything and you got 'divvy' as well! In other words a totally self sufficient little community that you only find nowadays in places that are hard to get to like Silverdale and Arnside, just north of Lancaster. Before we leave Wingates, how can anyone ever forget the "Bone Hole". Just down Slack Lane was a bone manufacturing works that probably made glue and gelatine. The animal carcasses were strewn around the yard and the stench was beyond belief. Any discussion regarding the weather at that time in Wingates, always included wind speed and direction! The local football team played their home matches on the Slack Lane pitch and were always worth at least two goals start!

Wingates Square is the home of the band room that houses Wingates band but also where most of my relatives lived. The band room was used for dances at the weekend and my sister, Teresa, remembers letting in the New Year on several occasions. Brass Band players were the stars of their community and Teresa remembers sitting on my dad's shoulders on the upper deck of an open topped bus, with the trophy held aloft, waving to the crowds who greeted the band following their success in a particular competition. Only one other band, namely Black Dyke Mills Band, has equalled Wingates feat of winning both the National Championships of Great Britain and the British Open in consecutive years, namely 1906/07. I know it's a long time ago but it's still a fantastic achievement.

Brass banding was at its peak during the first couple of decades of the 20th century and usually centred around mills, mines or churches. The factories or mines would employ people to play in their band because they were good musicians and not necessarily good at their job. I can just imagine it at Grimethorpe Colliery; they didn't bring up much 'nutty slack' but by gum they were a good band!

It is still a very popular but amazingly competitive hobby. I've never seen rivalry like it but once the competition's over they'll join each other at the bar for a pint or three. One of my favourite days' out is a trip to Saddleworth on Whit Friday. Saddleworth is an area that straddles Yorkshire and Lancashire and is full of small villages. On this particular day, each of the villages stage a brass band competition. Bands travel from all over the world to compete in these contests. Some play to win whilst others go to join in the occasion. It was a feature of the film "Brassed Off" and is well worth a visit.

There is a row of three houses opposite the Wingate's band room and my dad's mother purchased them for £200 in around 1900. She lived in one, her son next door and my mother's mother next to them. I used to go to the back door of the bakery and collect all grandmas' bread and barm cakes before the shop opened. Around the corner was a detached house where my dad's sister lived with her husband and sister; Aunt Hilda was very poorly as a child and the doctor gave her a few years to live. She moved in with her sister, my aunty Lily and lived into her 70's!

Aunty Lily and her husband John, together with Aunt Hilda were probably the richest people I knew! They had no overheads and no children so they became the focal point for every member of the Berry clan. Not because they had some money but because they were the most welcoming and generous people we knew. Every Sunday after mass for my family, and Morning service for everyone else, we'd meet at Aunty Lily's. After a cup of tea and a chat, the women would return home to cook dinner and the blokes went to the pub, generally the 'Greyhound' or Labour Club. Terribly sexist today but that was how it was back then.

Uncle John had quite a bit of land with his house and had a small orchard that we were allowed to 'raid' occasionally. He also owned two goats, Billy and Nanny, who were looked after by my sister Anne (Nanny) and cousin John (Billy).

Uncle John was the only person I knew that owned a car (registration GWH 594.... don't people remember stupid things). They also had a telly; we didn't get one of them until I was 12! I remember going to Aunt Lily's to watch Bolton Wanderers demolish Manchester United in the F.A. Cup final of 1958. It was probably the last time that the vast majority of the population were cheering on Man U. following the Munich tragedy. Not in Bolton though, and we cheered as the Lion of Vienna (Nat Lofthouse) fairly edged Harry Greg into the back of the net with his shoulder.

I didn't remember at the time how he got his famous nickname but it was to become so etched in the memory banks that we eventually recorded a song in his honour. It all happened in 1952 when England played Austria in the country's capital. The game was being watched by an Austrian crowd and the English contingent was made up of soldiers stationed in Europe following the aftermath of World War Two. The game was poised at 2-2 with "Lofty" already having scored one of England's goals. Tom Finney sent a through ball which Lofthouse latched on to. He ran 50 yards with the ball, during which time he was elbowed in the face, tackled from behind and finally tacked and knocked out by their goalkeeper. Too late though, the ball was in the back of the net! At the end of the game the pitch was invaded by hundreds of 'Tommies' who hoisted him aloft and hence a legend was born.

In the following year Lofthouse received the "Footballer of the Year" award on the evening prior to what is regarded as the greatest ever F.A. Cup Final. Although Nat scored a goal, he eventually ended on the losing team after another footballing superstar turned on a match winning performance. The final became known as the "Stanley Matthews Final" even though his team mate, Stan Mortenson scored a hat-trick.

Nat Lofthouse was capped 33 times by his country and during that period scored 30 goals which gave him one of the greatest goals per game ratio for any player to represent England. He scored a goal in a World Cup Quarter final (against Uruguay in 1954), was one of the first players to be inaugurated into the English Football's Hall of Fame in 2002. For his club, he cleaned other players' boots before becoming a player himself. Following his playing career he was assistant trainer, chief coach, caretaker and full time manager, chief scout, administrative manager, executive manager and in 1986 became president of his beloved Bolton Wanderers. As you've probably guessed, I'm a bit of a fan!

We didn't live 'up the Square' but just round the corner on Manchester Road, the A6, which was the main West coast trunk road to Scotland. The road always seemed busy and I'm sure it was, though not with as much traffic as today.

Our house was identical to many terraced cottages that held the proverbial two up two down. That's exactly what it was, upstairs two large bedrooms with no toilet, bathroom or running water. Downstairs we had the front room with coal fire and door that opened on to the A6! Maiden hanging from the ceiling, holding all the wet clothes which created a rainbow in the lobby! Back room contained a cooker, small pantry under the stairs and a large sink that had a "geyser" above it for hot water, large table and back door to the yard. This yard was a communal affair with dustbins housed in a block about 20 feet from the house. Between each dustbin shed was the outside 'lavvy' which regularly froze in winter unless a paraffin stove was left on overnight to protect the pipes. Toilet rolls were yesterday's Bolton Evening News. Outside the back door of each house was a coal bunker and tin bath hung on a 6 inch nail. There was no wall running at ninety degrees from our house to divide each yard so the area was quite clear. The toilet/bin block serviced our row and also the one that ran parallel on the other side, Thomas Street, so we had a full circle of yard to play in, it was a little bit similar to the chariot race in 'Ben Hur' and just as hazardous when we were on our bikes or trolleys made with a plank of wood and four pram wheels! All doors were left open and friends, relatives or anyone else for that matter had access to all the houses. We never knocked when we wanted our friends to come out to play. We just stood near their back door and shouted their names. If they wanted to join in they'd duly emerge and join in the fun, otherwise they'd stay indoors and ignore our screams!

I'd heard the term "back to back" houses and didn't really know what they were until fairly recently when I went into one. I know I'm being fairly stupid but they are exactly what it says on the label, 'back to back'; no back door, no back window, no back anything, only the back wall to the house on the other side. They still exist, in the beautiful village of Haworth in Yorkshire, home of the famous Bronte family.

My dad, as I said previously, worked at De Havilland, the aircraft manufacturers but he'd worked in various jobs over the years, including working down the pit and labourer for his brother Dick. He once tried to get in the police force but wasn't tall enough by a very small margin. He always said that if the interview had been earlier in the day he would be in the police force today. Apparently, he said, you were a bit taller in the morning after a good stretch in bed! My dad also worked in the 'Greyhound' at weekends to earn a few extra quid which he duly drank at the end of his shift.

His working day at De Havilland could be timed to the minute. After a cup of tea and a slice of bread and butter he'd leave the house at exactly the same time in the morning. I'm not quite sure what he did there, other than he was semi-skilled; does that mean he only knew half of what the skilled blokes knew or did it mean that he only half knew what to do? When the factory hooter sounded to mark the end of the working day, there were buses waiting outside, leaving immediately they were filled, which meant he arrived home at exactly the same time in the evening. During that time we owned a bull terrier dog by the name of 'Patch'. Patch was completely white apart from a blob of black fur around her eye, hence the name. She knew dad's routine as well, so when the time for his return home was due, she'd start to pace from the front door to the back. This pacing became a canter and eventually a gallop as father's footsteps approached (can dog's canter and gallop?). As the latch on the back door started to move, Patch somehow made sure she was at the front door. The door swung open as Patch sprinted the few yards separating them and, with a couple of feet to go, launched herself into the air. Similar to an Olympic event, dad closed the door, hung his hat on the hook, smiled at everyone and caught Patch at waist height, to be smothered by licks of affection from his favourite pooch!

I would occasionally go to the bus stop to meet him so that, for a couple of minutes at least, I had him all to myself. There was something tremendously reassuring about the aroma he brought from work. A mixture of grease, engines, sweat and cigarette smoke that intermingled to produce his own individual aroma. I used to think that lambs could find their mother's in exactly the same way; not that I used to go round smelling all the blokes that got off the bus!

On one particular evening we were all waiting at home for his arrival, so that we could all sit down to tea. Everything was going as normal, right up to the footsteps in the back yard and the slight sound of the latch moving. Patch, as usual, was at the front door, on her blocks, waiting for the starters' pistol. 'Click' goes the door, Patch starts to sprint, we all look to the door to acknowledge dad's arrival and we look in horror as Mrs. Cooper from next door appears at the doorway with a plate full of biscuits in her hand! Everything immediately reverts to slow motion as Mrs. Cooper, a frail lady in her mid seventies, calls out, "Is Amy in?" We slowly rise to our feet, my mother rushes towards Mrs. Cooper, we scream, "No, Patch!" but too late! Patch hits her around chest height and they both tumble into the back yard in a mass of fur, hair, biscuits and bone china! Needless to say, that was the last time Mrs. Cooper called round when Bob was due home from work.

My dad never once hit me but he was certainly in charge at home. Every night, after bouncing us on his knee to, "Ladies go to market chin, chin, chin, gentlemen go to market, trot, trot, trot, but the farmer behind with a bottle of wine goes nibblety, nobblety all the way home", I remember him saying, "Right boys, I'll count to ten and I want you in your beds!" We loved it! 1,2,3,4,.........8...., 8 and a half......nine....nine and a half ...nine and three quarters.....10! and we'd be in bed in the blink of an eye! Bed, an old double, with a flock mattress, which James and I shared. We'd make a divide between us by punching the stuffing into the middle! Not only did we share the bed, we shared the room with my mother and dad; they had another double bed opposite ours.

So the back bedroom was shared between Anne and Teresa, my two sisters, that is until one day there was a knock on the door and my Aunty May McGlone from Killorglin, County Kerry, together with her daughter Margaret paid us a visit. She wasn't really our aunt and I've no idea how they knew each other. They had come for a holiday and it was quite fascinating for us to hear their wonderful Irish brogue. When I say they'd come for a holiday, that's not quite true and we all realised this a few days later when Auntie May went out and got a job in the local hospital! They stayed for three years! So the room was then shared by my two sisters and our two visitors. I don't know if they paid rent or not, it wasn't something I needed to know. Sometime later, my mother's mother became ill and needed to stay with us. She couldn't get upstairs, not that there was any room up there anyway, so she slept in the front room, with eight more bodies upstairs. Good job we liked each other!

We prayed a lot more often for the next few years. After our tea we were required to kneel on the armchairs in the front room and say at least one decade of the rosary each night. I think my dad went to the pub when the rosary beads appeared. They seemed to be there all the time, both rosary beads and Aunty May, until one day, three years later, they left, never to return. We did visit them for a holiday when I was about 10 years old. Ours was actually a holiday, we left after a week! Apart from being in the middle of the country with farm animals given free range in the house I only remember one thing about my first visit to Ireland, 'Puck Fair'.

We arrived in the town of Killorglin and it was mayhem! Animals everywhere and statues of various saints covering every market stall which filled the streets. Apparently, someone goes into the hills nearby and wrestles a goat to a standstill. The animal is then brought into town, crowned 'king' by the 'Queen of the Fair', usually a young girl from a local school. The goat is then hoisted to the top of a massive scaffold where he is left for three days to survey his kingdom whilst all his subjects get drunk and sing a lot!

The fair has been traced back to the 1600's, maybe even to pagan times and is reputed to be the oldest non-religious festival in the world. It is thought to have pagan origins and the goat is a symbol of fertility and celebrates a good harvest. One theory is that a goat alerted the town to the approaching advance of Oliver Cromwell during his conquest of the country, although it is believed he never went as far west as the town. Whatever the reasons, it was granted legal status in 1603 by James the first of

England and Ireland (not, however of Scotland, as there were five more of them over the border...James' that is!). The locals aren't too bothered about its origins. All they care about is the fact that they are allowed to sing, dance and drink lots of beer for three days.

We sailed to and from Ireland overnight on the ferry and I vividly remember being in a bunk bed in a big cabin with many others. The journey was during a gale that gusted to force 8 and 9 and I spent the whole of the night being sick over someone's rucksack on the bunk below. At least it was their rucksack and not them!

I think that that was the only holiday I had as a child and I have a picture of two stick insects (me and my brother) on the beach somewhere on the west coast of Ireland to remember it by. My mother and Aunty May communicated by letter until Auntie May died and her daughter carried on the tradition after that, although, as far as I know, they never met again.

Just down the road from us lived my mother's three aunts, all sisters to her mother. They lived together and never married. Apparently two of them had boyfriends who were killed in the First World War and never looked for another man after that. Although they were devout Catholics they said that they were 'Quakers'. Their dress sense was immaculate and they wore stylish but sensible shoes, chic, tailored skirts and beautiful, though plain, silk blouses. Their hair was incredibly long but always brushed into a tight bun on their heads. They always reminded me of the film stars you would see in the old black and white films like Brief Encounter. They lived very frugally and never bought anything as frivolous as a birthday or Christmas card, never mind a present! Occasionally, however, quite out of the blue they'd ask if I wanted a pair of shoes or a suit. If you answered "No thanks!" then that was the end of it and the issue was never mentioned again, so we all learned to answer in the affirmative once the suggestion was made. It then became a military operation when all arrangements were meticulously adhered to. We'd meet at a certain time and walk to the Co-op down the street, always the Co-op and always the one down the street. There were two types of co-operatives, the 'friendly' and the 'equitable' They only shopped at the friendly and if there were two identical pairs of shoes but one was more expensive than the other we had to have the dearer ones.

They had lots of strange ways. They never had a television and only used the radio to listen to the Queen's speech on Christmas day. Aunt Amy smoked a cigarette whilst listening to the speech. She wasn't a smoker at all but this was a 'treat' for Christmas. It probably made her heave. They lived in a slightly smaller cottage than ours but with the same lack of amenities. Each sister had an all over wash each night before retiring and each was meticulously clean. When they died they passed their considerable wealth to the surviving sisters until only Aunt Amy was left. When she eventually passed away she left all the money that had been accumulated by the sisters over long lives to the Leprosy Society of Great Britain. Now, please correct me if I'm wrong, but I don't know of many lepers in Great Britain and even less in Wingates. Maybe strangeness runs in our family?

When mentioning Co-operative shops, you had to go down Market Street to see the full range. There was a butchers, general grocery shop, shoe shop, greengrocer, ladies drapery, cafe and confectioners, chemist, furnishing department, coal delivery service, and not forgetting the Co-operative Funeral Service. This meant that they not only provided everything for the populous during one's lifetime but after it as well!

Since the beginnings of time, mankind has co-operated with each other for their own mutual benefit but in 1884, twenty-eight weavers started the Rochdale Society of Equitable Pioneers. This is considered to be the best and most successful model for modern day co-operatives, although by no means, the first one. Within 10 years there were over 1,000 co-operative societies in Britain. If you drive into Rochdale from the motorway, you drive under a bridge which displays the notice 'Birthplace of Co-operation'. Turn in the opposite direction from the motorway and you enter Oldham. Going under a similar bridge you see the wonderful notice, 'Welcome to Oldham, home of the tubular bandage!'...........not a lot going on in Oldham!

Five

Saturday Cowboys

We'd go down the street at least once a week and that was on Saturday morning when we visited the 'Empire' cinema. The town boasted two picture houses, the other one being the 'Rink' off Church Street. Myself and my brother attended the Saturday morning club watching the likes of Hopalong Cassidy, The Lone Ranger, Lassie and Flash Gordon with Ming the Merciless. Flash Gordon's so old now that they just call him 'Gordon'. What always amazed me was that at the end of each show, the Lone Range, Flash Gordon or Hopalong fell, ran or was pushed off the edge of a cliff or into a fire, river or somewhere equally horrible. They are falling to earth as the voice in the background states, "Will he survive, can he escape the clutches of the villain, have we seen the last of him. Find out next week when we join the fantastic adventure of ....whoever!"

So all week we worry if he is going to survive, how can he escape from a fall when he's half way down the cliff, how can he escape from the fire when most of his clothes have been incinerated, how will he not drown when he's been under the water for twenty minutes? Then the show starts and Flash never even reaches the edge of the cliff, never mind being halfway down the precipice, The Lone Ranger never actually gets his shirt burned before he escapes and Hopalong actually escapes before even getting his socks wet! But we loved every minute! I know 'Hoppy' was a very clean cut cowboy and always behaved admirably, so he might not be too pleased with what we used to do on a Saturday morning. Sometimes we actually sneaked into the 'flicks' by way of an open window (Sorry Hoppy!)... The trouble was that the only window we could get through led us into the ladies lavatory, which wasn't a problem unless the cubicle was occupied. I never had any trouble but one or two of my mates ended up on a girl's lap trying to get in for nothing!

The greatest moment of my trips to the cinema was when the Ten Commandments came to town. This was a major coup for this small picture house and so they made the most of it. There were banners erected that spanned Market Street stating, 'The Ten Commandments come to Westhoughton'. I don't know whether this was an insinuation that we were a heathen lot or not! The film, starring Charlton Heston as Moses, was a major event and everyone talked about it for a couple of weeks prior to its arrival. We got up early on the Saturday morning and made our way to the Empire. Saturday morning club had been cancelled that week to accommodate the children who wanted to see De Mille's masterpiece. On arrival, there was a queue all the way round the corner from the picture house. It was probably three times the normal queue length with much noise and excitement. When the doors opened and we began to approach the front of the line we could hear quite a commotion. 'Chinese whispers' quickly informed us of the quandary; they were charging everybody two shillings instead of the normal tanner, four times the normal admission fee! Well, of course, I didn't have that princely sum on me so I panicked. I was a mile from home and it wasn't guaranteed that my dad would give me so much money, even if I managed to get there and back in time. I had two choices, try my luck or forget the parting of the Red Sea! No contest! I set off at my fastest speed, not forgetting that this was a marathon, I had to get home, yes, but then I had to get back again. Was I going to make it, only one way to find out, keep going, keep going. That's two lampposts, nearly at the railway station, just up to the paper shop, "Good morning Mrs. Jones, can't stop, Moses is waiting for me!", past Seddon Street, two more lamp-posts and I'm there. With lungs bursting I eventually make it home and gasping air I try to explain to dad the problem.

"How bloody much!" was his reply? This was the expected answer, now I had to wait to see if he would come up with the goods.

"I hope you don't expect this again because you'll not get it!" and he tosses me half a crown! "You'll need an ice cream after all that running!"

"Thanks dad!" and I'm off again. Mostly downhill going back, no idea what the time is, I'll see the church clock when I get round this bend! I think I'm going to make it!

In an almost state of collapse I get to the end of Church Street and turn the corner to see the Empire. There's a couple of people loitering outside while the rest of the street is bustling with shoppers. I go to the kiosk and look up at the bloke and then panic hits me; it might be sold out and I'll miss the greatest event ever to hit Westhoughton!

"What's wrong lad, you look as if you've seen a ghost. You'd better hurry up, it's nearly started. That'll be sixpence!"

"Sixpence! You told me it was two bob!"

"It was at first but nobody had enough money so we dropped the price"

I didn't know whether to laugh or cry! After a while I had a little chuckle to myself because I could give dad his money back. Relax Tony, enjoy Cecil B. De Mille's classic. Don't worry about missing Flash Gordon; he'll be back next Saturday.

Nothing could beat the pictures on a Saturday morning because we didn't have a telly so we could see things that otherwise we could only imagine. When we had a couple of pennies spare we might have a ride to Horwich and go up the 'Pike'. Rivington Pike is a picturesque tower on the edge of the West Pennine moors and is used to describe the area in general. The pike was originally a signal tower where fires were lit to inform the region as an early warning system, originally of raids from marauding Scots, then the invasion of the Spanish Armada, the end of World War One, the Queen's Silver Jubilee in 1977 and the dawning of the Millennium. I'm sure it must have been lit in 1958 to celebrate the Wanderers win at Wembley against some team from Manchester!

Six

Rivington

Nearly everyone from this region knows the area as it is a magnet for ramblers, bikers, dog walkers and cyclists. The whole area was bought at the start of the 1900's by local philanthropist and general 'good egg' William Hesketh Lever. He made his money by keeping us all clean! He began the Lever Brothers dynasty together with his brother who was only a bit player in the scheme of things. Lever decided that we would be more likely to keep ourselves clean if the soap we used was pleasant to the skin and sense of smell and so invented 'Sunlight' soap. He built the model village of Port Sunlight on the Wirral for his workers, together with, as the name suggests, a port to send his products around the world. The village included a church, school, shop, theatre, social club, a canteen providing subsidised meals, an open air swimming pool, gymnasium and various societies for those interested in art, music and literature. Each block of houses had its' own architect and was individually designed which made it the envy of most working class families. Unusually, he insisted that the bathroom should be near the front door, so that when dirty workers returned home they could jump straight into the bath!

He expanded his business empire to encompass, not only the soap making but all the raw materials needed to make soap. He bought vast tracts of land in what was the Belgian Congo to grow palm oil. In today's world Lever would be depicted as a very racist person but it could be argued that during his lifetime he was extremely benevolent. Not only did he pay his native African workers more than anyone else he also built houses and schools for the workers and their children. In contrast to this attitude you need only look at what was happening in America...let's not just blame America! It happened throughout Europe. In 1906, Ota Benga, a pygmy from the Congo, was brought to Bronx Zoo in New York and stuck in a cage with a chimpanzee and advertised as an evolutionary inferior race with the cage sign depicting 'The missing Link'. This is during the lifetime of my grandfather and the year before my own dad was born! Thank God some things have changed!

Lever was born in Bolton, so, as his business interest boomed, he bought the area around Rivington and built a holiday bungalow for himself and his wife. He built a wooden bungalow on the hillside and planted Japanese gardens, Roman bridges and the famous Pigeon Tower. The gardens have always been known to locals as the 'Chinese' gardens for some unknown reason. In its' heyday the house hosted balls, garden parties and public open days. The locals loved it because Lever had his own zoo which housed wallabies, zebras and even a lion cub and the ornamental ponds had their own flock of flamingos. The wooden bungalow was destroyed by an arson attack in 1913 when a suffragette known as Edith Rigby destroyed it. It's ironic because Lever was a great supporter of the suffragette movement. The structure was replaced by a stone building which fell into disrepair following his death in 1925. Before it was finally demolished it was used as a billet for troops during the Second World War. One interesting fact before we leave Lord Leverhulme is that several of his bedrooms had only three walls. Not a triangle as you might think but a square construction with one wall missing! He was a fresh air fiend and liked to sleep in his own bed, in his own bedroom but outside! I wouldn't like to imagine what guests he had during the night?

We visited 'Rivvy', as we called it, all year round but the main event of the year was on Good Friday. For miles around, on that day, people would leave their houses as far afield as Westhoughton, Atherton, Bolton and Chorley and walk all the way to Horwich before ascending the 'Pike'. Thousands upon thousands made the trek and the lower slopes of the hills were filled with fairground attractions. Maybe this pilgrimage started as some sort of re-enactment of Christ's last hours on Calvary but we saw it as a highlight of our year. We'd set off quite early from home with our bottles of water and sugar butties joining other groups of kids who were going the same way. It took an eternity to get there (it's about 5 or 6 miles) and then we had to climb up the Pike. For some unknown reason I always bought a small bow and arrow whilst up there and spent the rest of the day hiding in the rhododendrons, firing at unsuspecting passersby. By this stage we'd run ourselves to a standstill and it was time to get home to get ready for church. I can't remember ever walking home because we were so tired. There was always a queue of buses waiting to take everyone back to where they came from.

Seven

School

My recollections of early schooling are somewhat
blurred. I attended a small Catholic School, Sacred Heart,
in Westhoughton. It was strange in the fact that pupils
attended from five to fifteen, when they left to find work.
At fifteen, pupils left without taking any exams
whatsoever and looking back it's amazing how some of
those students ever survived.

Miss Fairhurst was a terrifying spectacle, everyone
was petrified of her. I remember one of my first days at
school when I needed to go to the toilet and she refused
me permission so I didn't ask twice. Miss had to send for
my sister Teresa, to help clear the mess, when I did it in
my pants! I once answered her back but, instead of giving
me the cane (although she preferred the rounder's bat),
she told me to stand in the corner for the remainder of the
class. I dutifully went over to take up my position, which
just happened to be in front of her classroom cupboard
which housed work books, pencils, rubbers, scissors and

on one shelf, a packet of Polo mints. I was supposed to ponder on my conduct and contemplate how I could improve my behaviour but all I could think of was these Polo mints in front of my eyes. The longer the class went on the more the craving engulfed me until I eventually thought, "Bugger it, she'll never know!" and proceeded to cram a couple of the offending mints into my drooling mouth. I know I shouldn't have done it and I know I was in the corner for punishment but I just couldn't help it! For years after, if the anecdote ever came to mind, I felt terribly guilty and this is the first time that anyone has been told of my misdemeanour – please don't tell Miss Fairhurst!

There were plusses and minuses having older sisters at the same school. If they couldn't defend you they knew someone who could, so on several occasions Tommy Gorringe came to my aid. They always say that no other word in the English language rhymes with orange but Tommy's surname does. He could probably have made it as a professional footballer being easily the best goalkeeper for miles around. He had a small handicap, however; he was a total nutcase, and if anything on the field displeased him he would sort it out with his fists. I've seen him chasing other players around the pitch with his own team mates and the referee behind trying to stop him – a bit like the Keystone Cops or Benny Hill.

I had a few fights, lost some, won some but I don't think I was particularly maltreated by my peers. Some of the older boys tried it on once or twice but when they knew Tommy was my sister's friend all hostilities ceased!

I do remember the food and drink at school; we still had a small bottle of milk each in those days (a third of a pint). I always loved it on a winter's morning when the bottles had frozen, so the crates were placed on top of the radiators. The tops had come off because the frozen milk had expanded (I must have learned something about science after all!). The radiators then started their work and by the time we got at them the tops were lovely, warm and creamy....delicious. Unfortunately that couldn't be said for the food. It came at about 10 a.m. every morning in big containers that acted like flasks. Not only did they keep the food warm but they continued cooking it for another couple of hours. By the time we got a plate full, it was a boiled up mess. We had to eat it though. Dinner ladies would stand over us until our plates were clean. I must admit I did quite like the sago and semolina puddings with a dollop of jam on the top. You mixed it up until it became a pink sludge then guzzled it all down. I probably enjoyed it because we very rarely had a sweet at home. Things like oranges were a treat at Christmas and very rarely seen any other time. One thing we did used to get was pomegranates. I have no idea why but it took us ages to eat one as we had to spear each tiny little segment with a needle.

I sailed through Sacred Heart because I was reasonably bright, or should I say, I thought I was. It took a few years before I realised that I was not the Brain of Britain. We didn't have many exams and if we only stayed until the age of fifteen then we left school with no qualifications so the teachers didn't appear to be too concerned about teaching us much. I wouldn't say that about Miss Fairhurst but would definitely mean it about Mr. Liddell. He used to come to school in odd shoes and if anyone mentioned this they got a board duster slung at them when they weren't looking. During P.E. he would play cricket during summer and football in winter. He refereed the football matches and joined in when he felt like it. Cricket, however was another story. He decided who was to bat or bowl, then proceeded either to open the bowling or the batting. No-one else got a chance. Even when he was clean bowled he became umpire and ruled it a 'no ball'. On one occasion he hit the ball high in the air and Michael Purtill came to catch it. Unfortunately he lifted his hands in the air in preparation but the ball went straight through and knocked him out!

We'd play a game where we divided into two teams; one team formed a line at right angles to a wall, leaning on each other's backs. Then the opposition proceeded to run towards the line and leap frog as far forward as possible landing as hard as they possibly could in order to break the chain that had been formed. The toughest were nearest the wall to take the strain as the opposition tried to land on your back from the greatest height. That sounds really stupid, it probably was but we enjoyed playing it.

At home we played 'kick out can'; it was usually called 'kick out ball' but we could never afford a ball, so an old tin can took its place. You drew a circle, placed the can in it, kicked it as far as you could then went and hid. Whoever was 'it' had to retrieve the can and put it back in the circle. When they'd done that they had to come and find you. Once spotted they ran back as fast as possible to the circle and 'tig' you out. If you were a faster runner you could get back to the circle before him and you kicked out the can and started all over again.

At around the age of 11, I was instructed by the Headmaster, Mr. Abbott, that I would be taking my Eleven plus exam for entry to the Catholic Grammar school in Bolton. Thornleigh Salesian College was a school run by the Salesian order of priests. They are an order founded in the back streets of Turin by Don Boscoe whose whole ethos was that the priests should employ teaching methods based on love rather than punishment. Somehow I think that last bit got lost in translation from Italian but more of that later.

I was told that the exam would take place at any time and I was not to know when, so that I wouldn't be nervous. From that moment onwards, every time I had a question paper stuck in front of my nose I panicked! Then I was told that if I passed the exam it didn't really matter because I would have to take an entrance exam for the school as well. Great, more reason to panic!

Eventually I forgot that I had to take my exam at school, so it came and went without my knowing. Following the results I was called from my desk one morning by Mr. Abbott. He addressed me as Anthony Berry; the only time in my life I can remember being called Anthony. He said he would use my 'Sunday' name because I had passed with flying colours. I wasn't sure how to feel because I would be going to a school where I knew nobody except John Hesketh and Eddie Marsh who passed the exam as well (the best result Sacred Heart had ever had). Then I remembered I still had to sit the entrance exam!

Eight

Grammar School

Both my mother and dad accompanied me to Astley Bridge in Bolton for the exam. I remember walking through the arch that was the entrance to the school. Above the arch was a statue of 'Mary Help of Christians'. I wasn't to know that at the time but if I had, I would have been saying many decades of the rosary to her. I remember one question in the exam that I had no idea of the answer. It was algebra and I don't think that my teachers in Westhoughton had ever heard of that subject. It was the type that said if "a" is 6 and "b" is 3, what is "x" worth. I had absolutely no idea. It nearly flummoxed me for the rest of the paper because I kept rereading the question instead of getting on with it. Mary Help of Christians must have heard my cries for help because I duly passed.

My first day at Thornleigh was an eye opener. Everybody had a uniform, something I'd never seen before as none of the schools in Westhoughton used a uniform, probably because their parents couldn't afford to buy them. The school required pupils to wear short trousers until the 3rd year. These were accompanied by grey, knee length socks, a white shirt and brown blazer and tie. Many years later I remember a friend who said he used to go to the Senior Lads (the local High School) in a Mac and wellies – Just a Mac and wellies, nothing else because money was so scarce.

I walked under Mary Help of Christians and made my way to the playground, an absolutely massive area of tarmac, probably the size of 5 or 6 football pitches. Standing in the middle of this mass of humanity I wondered what I had let myself in for. Then some teachers appeared and they were in uniform as well, cassocks to be precise... now that's not swearing...... it's the uniform of a Salesian priest but added to the cassock was an extra 'cloak' over the shoulders which they would flick to effect some statement that they'd made. Not only the priests but all the other teachers who weren't priests had a uniform as well. It consisted of a 'Zorro' cloak but I never saw any of them with a sword!

They all had nicknames, Sid, Tex, Sam, Ratbag, Jock, Taffy etc. And these names were generally given for a reason. Tex was an Irishman with a drolling accent that sounded just like John Wayne, hence the name. 'Ratbag' was aptly named because everyone hated him. He was a vicious monster who beat the kids with relish. I suppose it was for their own good. It never did me, did me, did me any harm! I was to find out, many years later, during a week-long school trip to one of the sister colleges near London, that 'Ratbag' was quite a kind and pleasant human being but once in school the Mr. Hyde side of his character came out again and Dr. Jekyll was left in London.

Several of the priests used snuff instead of smoking tobacco. They would regularly take a 'pinch' during class. I can still see their soggy, orange handkerchiefs following the sneezing bout that the snuff induced.

I remember sitting in class, near the window, one day and 'Tex' came strolling through the playground three floors below. Over his shoulder was a twelve bore shotgun. I thought that one of my schoolmates must have behaved really badly. I breathed a sigh of relief when he took his anger out on the magpies that filled the trees surrounding the playground!

'Taffy', would you believe, was Welsh and had a disgusting tendency to produce copious amounts of saliva which, during class, ended up on the open pages of kids sitting on the front row. Not only were these students punished by being placed at the front of the class but they got the cane because their schoolwork became illegible when pools of saliva, mixed with the ink, produced works of modern art instead of the French homework that was originally on the page.

One day, John Gallagher had forgotten his homework, again! The teacher seemed to be amazingly reasonable about the whole issue. He calmly strolled over to John, sitting in the front row and said a few words; then out of the blue he punched him in the face, kicked him to the back of the class and proceeded to knee, kick and punch him until he became a bloodied mess. Eventually he allowed John up and calmly asked him to leave the room. John stood up and walked, with some difficulty, to the door shouting, "I'll get you! I'm going to the headmaster to make a complaint". John disappeared and the incident was never again mentioned. This physical punishment appears cruel and appalling in today's society but it was the norm in those days. Not that I'm condoning it but what I'm trying to say is that it wasn't peculiar to my school alone; all my mates who attended other schools would tell similar tales. I recently watched a play on television which told a story of a young Irish girl who had become pregnant and was forced to move to a school run by nuns. The Victorian building was run in a Victorian way with Victorian attitudes. The girls were beaten and treated like third class citizens and throughout the play I kept thinking that thank god that this appalling behaviour has long been consigned to the history books. Then I listened to the music that was playing in the background........it was The Beatles! Maybe things have improved far quicker than I thought?

Anyone who attended my school during this era, when recollecting teachers, would mention only one person. The schools' music teacher and Celtic supporter was a priest nicknamed 'Jock'. Music and football were the only things in his life that mattered. I'm sure the priesthood meant something to him but it never came across to any of us. He taught us music, coached the football team and taught us Celtic chants. If you were a decent musician or excelled in sport then you had a chance, otherwise there was the strong possibility that you could be thrown through a window!

He was also a motorbike fan and owned some old B.S.A., Triumph, Norton, or other equally famous machine. I remember him telling us, after the accident, about the journey he had to make to Cheshire to collect some instrument that he desperately needed to enhance the brass band. He'd taught all day, done choir practice followed by band rehearsal after school, eaten a bite of something and travelled down to pick up the said instrument. He climbed back on his bike, drove all the way back to Astley Bridge, and at the last turn before school, had run straight into a brick wall! Prayers were said at school for the next few months as he had been severely injured; broken skull, broken pelvis, broken arm, but as they say in the old movies, not a broken spirit! I'll never forget, on his return to school, arm, leg and head in plaster, the first thing he did was go straight to the music room to rehearse the choir for an up and coming show.

So here was the Brain of Britain in the midst of all these boys; did I mention that it was an all boy's school? It wasn't long before my illusions of grandeur were to be shattered. They began to teach me about things I'd never heard of before; science, algebra, psychology but worst of all French and Latin. I had a lot of time to think about how stupid I was on my journeys to and from school. It took about an hour and a half each way and cost four pence halfpenny per journey.

There was a bus straight to Wingates from Bolton but it was only every hour, so I would occasionally catch the bus to Westhoughton town centre and walk up Church Street. This was when another problem began to occur. Several boys of my age and older lived on the route home from the town centre. One or two of them felt that by wearing a school uniform I was a perfect target for name calling and worse. It led to many months of fear that culminated in me knocking seven colours out of the perpetrators. I had to get them one at a time because I couldn't cope with a gang. I'll never forget when they once pounced on me and carried me over to some waste land, tied me to a tree and pelted me with wild tomatoes that grew round the pond. I eventually wriggled free and jumped over a fence that I had never been able to scale before, or since for that matter.

I ran home to be greeted by my dad, "What the bloody hell's happened to you?" I was covered in mud, dirt and tomato pips so I had to tell him. He raced down Church Street promising to murder the gang........happy days!

Recently, when reminiscing with my sister, we talked about dad. As Westhoughton was only a small town, everyone knew each other. Being quite nosey he wanted to know the 'low-down' on anyone we brought home. When Mary Marsh came home one day, dad commented, "And what's your name?"

"Mary Marsh" she answered.

"And what is your mother's name?"

"She's Mary as well".

"And what was her name before she got wed?"

"I think it was Mary", came the reply!

Life continued in a fairly serene sort of way for the next few years. I didn't do too well in my first years' exams and was relegated from the class I was in to the 'thickies' class. The intake in school at that time was approximately 100 per year which made three classes of just over thirty. They were Alpha, Beta and Gamma, Alpha being the Arts (English, History, Art, Geography etc.) and Beta being the Sciences of Maths Physics, Chemistry, Biology etc. Then came Gamma where the dregs of the schools society were placed. That's where I was and that was where I was to stay until sixth form. I made quite a few friends and although it was very strict, I must say I quite enjoyed my time at Thornleigh. I got used to walking down the street every morning and sharing the bus ride with Eddie Marsh. He was exactly the same as me in the mornings, horrible! This suited us both as we would grunt a greeting then sit all the way to Bolton without communicating at all.

One morning in class I saw John Hesketh, the third of our trio who passed the exam, sleeping. John was a Wayne Rooney type of build, extremely strong and adult, so nobody messed with him. I, however, had known him for years and thought it would be really funny to waken him by tickling his ears. Big mistake! John sort of exploded from the desk and in one movement hoisted me in the air and onto the window ledge at the back of the class. Unfortunately he pushed a little too hard, broke the window and sent me flying into space. The room was two floors up and as I began to recite the last rites for the repose of my soul, he caught hold of me by the lower legs and hoisted me back into the room. Even the teacher was flabbergasted and could only mutter some sort of admonishment to John. He became a sort of hero to me because although he'd tried to kill me, he'd saved my life as well!

On one of my first music classes the pupils were asked if they would like to join the brass band. I thought I might give it a go and asked what I had to do. I was directed to the instrument cupboard and told to choose something to play. The only thing left on the shelves when I got there was a trombone and that was how I became the worst trombone player the school had ever known. "Take it home and practise", I was told. Unfortunately I didn't really know how to practise as I couldn't get a note out of the thing, couldn't read music and had absolutely no idea where to start. After several years I could eventually read the music but as I had never had an individual lesson I didn't improve much from that day on.

The band would get the occasional engagement and we travelled to various halls in the region but my favourite 'gigs' were either summer fairs or religious marches. Every year we did the 'Whit Walks' in Manchester. We were always employed for the day by St. Malachy's church in Collyhurst. We marched and played from the church, into the city centre, round the streets a bit, then back to Collyhurst. By the time we returned we were all exhausted but it was always an enjoyable day, the best parts of which were going under bridges! As we approached a bridge 'Jock', our music teacher, always told us to get out 'Slaidburn'. It's one of the most popular march tunes and as we reached the bridge we tried to reach the crescendo at the same time. Everyone's ears would ring as the acoustic of the bridge caused the volume to increase tenfold and would make the hairs on the back of your neck bristle!

I was also a member of the choir and always remember a fellow student. Steve Kelly was a member of the choir and orchestra but not through choice. It was well known that Steve had 'Perfect Pitch' which means he could reproduce a note without any help whatsoever. In other words, if I sing any note, a person with this gift can tell you exactly what note you are singing. Most people see this as a wonderful gift but some might see it as a handicap because any note played or sung that isn't perfectly in tune would be like hearing someone scraping their nails on a blackboard and can be physically painful to a person with perfect or absolute pitch. We worked with a guy once who told us that 'Perfect Pitch' was having a free accommodation at your girlfriend's pub!

Steve was an incredible musician but had absolutely no interest in it whatsoever. We were preparing to learn a new choral piece which we hadn't seen before. Jock handed Steve the music and told him to sing it without any help including a guide note. Steve sang it from beginning to end in perfect annotation, dynamics and pitch. The class were quite amazed and Jock pulled out a few more hairs from his head because he could see such talent and all Steve could think about was leaving school and working on his dad's market stall!

Sport is a great love of mine and I played for the school football and basketball teams. For the first couple of years at school we had a cricket coach whose name I vaguely recalled...............Gary Sobers! Amazingly we were coached by probably the best all-round cricketer the world has ever known. Many years later, in 1968, playing for Nottinghamshire against Glamorgan, I remember him knocking the unfortunate Malcolm Nash for six sixes in one over becoming the first player in the sport to perform the feat. Not only could he bat but he was a brilliant slow and medium paced bowler as well. He must have been brilliant at spinning the ball as he had six fingers on each hand! Apparently he was born with the extra fingers but removed them himself with some catgut and a sharp knife when he was a young boy! They were tough in those days! Things have changed somewhat over the years.

I recall, only the other day whilst listening to the football commentary on our local radio station. Two players go in for a tackle and the commentator says, "That was a terrific tackle! They bounced off each other like a pair of rhinos!" I'm thinking, it's as hard now as it's ever been as the commentator continues, "And Berbatov is walking back up the pitch adjusting his 'Alice' band!" What would Tommy Smith, the Liverpool legend, have thought of that? At the time he played for Liverpool, there was a lovely story about the sign outside the church asking "What would you do if Christ came to

Liverpool?" and some bright spark had written underneath "Move St. John to inside right!"

*Ian St. John played centre forward for Liverpool 424 times during the 60's and scored 118 goals.

Nine

Home Life

At the age of about twelve we were forced to leave Manchester Road, as the house was compulsorily purchased by the council so that the road could be widened. My parents were offered the princely sum of £690 for the house that held so many memories. And so we moved to ....Wingates (do you think we could go any farther!) We moved to a house next door to the Windmill pub - nothing much changed apart from the fact that this house had a bathroom! No inside toilet but let's not be too greedy! We had a bath and a small garden, absolute luxury! By this time my sister Teresa had married and inherited the best name on earth - she became Teresa (trees-a) Forrest! Anne had started work as a nurse so she lived on site at the Royal Albert Edward Infirmary in Wigan. When she finished her training she went on to become a Midwife, eventually becoming District Midwife for the area. Because she needed to contact people we acquired a telephone! Not much use to any of us because we didn't know anyone with a phone!

When I think of something like that, it brings to mind Notts County who were the very first football team in the world. If they were the first football team in the world who did they play against?

Dad worked regular nights at the De-Havilland factory at Lostock so we only saw him before he went to work in the evening for a few hours. He went to bed very early in the morning so we didn't usually see each other then. However, he told me one evening, that a world championship boxing match was to take place 'live' on telly at about 4.30a.m. He said he would wake me up early so that I could watch Cassius Clay, who was now known as Muhammad Ali, take on Sonny Liston, in a re-match of an earlier fight that Ali won in the seventh round. It was quite exciting being able to spend some time with my dad alone as it was an extremely rare occurrence, what nowadays is referred to as 'quality time'. He woke me at about twenty past four with a cup of tea and said that the fight was about to start. I walked downstairs bleary eyed to be told that the fight was over, Ali had knocked Liston out in the first round with what was to be known as his 'Phantom Punch', in other words he didn't really hit him but Liston still ended up on the canvas for a count of ten!

In 1967, Ali was to be stripped of his title after refusing to join the army and fight in Vietnam because of his religious beliefs. He came out with the immortal line..... "No Vietcong ever called me nigger!" I didn't think about it at the time but people like Ali, Martin Luther King, Nelson Mandela and others were changing the world as we knew it because of their actions. After

Ali won the gold medal at light heavyweight at the 1960 Olympic Games, he returned home to celebrate at a local restaurant. He was refused entry because he was black. Ali took his gold medal and flung it into the Ohio River in protest. Many years later he was presented with a replacement medal at the 1996 Olympics in Atlanta.

He was born Cassius Marcellus Clay after his father, who in turn was named after a man of the same name whom his ancestors worked for. Cassius Marcellus Clay was a Southern aristocrat and slave owner who became an anti-slavery campaigner. He was a 19th Century Republican Politician and worked as Minister to Russia from 1863 – 1869, during which time he was a major influence in negotiations for the purchase of Alaska from the Russian Empire at a cost of $7.2 Million, which equates to two cents per acre! Clay began publishing an anti-slavery newspaper titled 'True American' which caused him to receive several death threats. His premises were eventually attacked by over 60 protestors and his printing machinery was sent to Cincinnati, Ohio.... probably saved him the cost of shipping it there himself!

The sixties were an amazing period of time, with John F. Kennedy becoming the youngest ever President of the United States in the first year of that decade. The following year the Berlin wall was erected to prevent people from East Berlin attempting to defect to the West, Yuri Gagarin is the first person in space and South Africa leave the Commonwealth and adopt an Apartheid policy of Government.

As that decade moves swiftly along, Martin Luther King had a dream that one day his children would be judged, not by the colour of their skin but by the content of their character. I share the same birthday as this wonderful human being and his birthday is a public holiday in America. He got involved in the Civil Rights movement eight years prior to this when one of his parishioners, Rosa Parks, caused a major commotion and was arrested after refusing to give up her seat on the bus for a white passenger. This became the seminal moment that began the relentless quest for equality for black people in America.

Other things were moving at a relentless pace during the decade besides the Civil Rights movement. Christian Barnard performed the first heart transplant in Cape Town. It was reported that he was assisted by a self taught black African surgeon called Hamilton Naki although he wasn't there at the time. Naki had no formal training but did assist Barnard in some operations. Barnard is reported to have said that he was technically far better than him.

Neil Armstrong walked on the moon and the Woodstock festival took place in New York when 300,000 spend three days advocating peace, love and music. Probably the most monumental event of the 60's was the assassination of John F. Kennedy in Dallas and Pele coming to Bolton!

During the '66 World Cup, Brazil were stationed in Bolton and trained on Bolton's training ground at Bromwich Street. The public were allowed inside the ground and the people of Bolton were utterly amazed to see Edson Arantes do Nascimento (Pele's real name)........that's another one of those useless facts that I recall. I might remind you that although I had to check it, I spelt it right! Maradonna was good, but nowhere near as good as the master from Brazil! My reasoning for this is not based on footballing skills alone (on that basis I still think he was the best!) but, on the general attitude to the sport and the society in which they lived. Pele was a brilliant role model and became a worldwide ambassador for football and is revered throughout the footballing world. This cannot be said of Maradona and brilliant though he was, I can still see the little cheat's hand rise higher than Peter Shilton's....... 'Hand of God'..... rubbish!..........'Hand of Cheat' as far as I'm concerned!

Brazil played all their first round matches at Goodison Park, home of Everton and were kicked off the pitch by Portugal. It was Brazil's worst ever performance in a World Cup and although they beat Bulgaria (2-0), they lost to Hungary (3-1) and Portugal (3-1) and didn't get past the first round. In that particular World Cup the star of the show was Portugal's Eusebio. During their quarter final against North Korea, they went three nil down and the 'Black Panther', as he was nicknamed, came to the fore and scored four goals. Portugal eventually finished third in the competition and Eusebio scored nine goals in total, making him the leading scorer. They eventually lost to us in the semis and we went on to win the competition, just in case you'd forgotten!

Shortly after the Liston fight, in May of that year, dad came home from work looking exhausted. Mother said, "You're not going to work tomorrow looking like that!" He'd never missed a day's work in over 30 years but on this occasion he took heed of my mother's threat. He was, sadly, never to return to work again. Within fourteen weeks he had died of lung cancer. On the morning of his death all the family were gathered around his bed which had been moved downstairs. All I could think of at that poignant time was that his toe nails needed cutting.

Immediately he took his last breath, there was a knock on the front door and the vicar from St. John's church at Wingates was calling to see how dad was. He gave his blessing and last rites and was a daily visitor until after the funeral, becoming an absolute rock for my mother. This wouldn't seem unusual today but in the mid-sixties religions didn't mix and this was a greatly encouraging sign of things to come.

I'll never forget one particular morning, before dad's funeral, when several of my mother's female friends called by to support her. Stories were told and happy times recounted. At one point in the proceedings everyone burst into laughter and one of them joked, "Who'd believe we're getting ready for a funeral!" Friends are wonderful things and my mother had loads of them.

Following the allotted time that is required for mourning mum also had a multitude of suitors, after her hand in marriage. She was only fifty-two and so would make a 'good catch'. After each of their visits we used to laugh at their inadequacies. Most were lonely widowers who needed female companionship in their later years. Mother always said, "Don't worry, there's no chance of me getting married again. Once was more than enough".

Up until that time my mother had been a housewife and mother and had never had paid employment. I'm quite sure that was something to do with the male machismo which saw man as the main provider and the woman's place being in the home. A representative from De Havilland had attended dad's funeral and said that if mother ever needed a job, just give him a call. Can you see that happening nowadays? Several years later she made that call and was immediately offered a job in 'West Block', the secret side of the aerospace industry, where she had to sign the official secrets act, before beginning work as a maker of tiny micro chip components for missiles. But I didn't know that because it was a secret!

Money was tight and mother decided to apply for a council house and to sell the house on Chorley Road. It had cost them the enormous sum of £1,000.00 to buy and when a bloke offered her £1,500.00 she couldn't refuse. He turned up at the front door one night with the fifteen hundred quid in a plastic bag and handed it over to mum. They shook hands on the deal and several weeks later we moved 'down the street' to 1,The Avenue (great address) and, for the first time in my life had an inside toilet, pure, unadulterated luxury! No more rolled up newspaper set on fire to guide your way to the outside 'lavvy'.

There had been a major boom in Council House building following the Second World War after almost four million homes had been damaged or destroyed by bombs. Social housing in Britain started around the 10th Century when 'Almshouses' were built for the *poor, old and distressed folk'*. Until the Industrial Revolution that was the only source of Social housing. However, during the 1800's, philanthropists like William Lever built entire villages for their workforce. These can still be seen in places like Saltaire, in West Yorkshire, Bournville to the South of Birmingham and Port Sunlight on the Wirral. It wasn't until 1885 that the state took an interest by having a Royal Commission but this didn't become compulsory until the Housing Act of 1919 which required councils to provide affordable housing mainly for the working classes.

Our house was on a very small estate and was opposite our church so it meant that I could attend every service from Sunday mass to Wednesday Benediction and anything else Father O'Leary could find for me to do!

Ten

Scouts

Prior to working at De Havilland, which became Hawker Siddeley which became British Aerospace, mother got a job as cleaner to Sir Geoffrey and Lady Hulton. They were quite a pleasant couple and I met them several times, at church but especially as a member of the local scout troop. Sir Geoffrey was the Head chaplain of the Scouting movement in Great Britain and we used to go to Hulton Park to camp for the odd weekend.

Camping was one of the main pastimes of the Scouting movement founded by Robert Baden-Powell. His sister, Agnes, was responsible for the birth of Guiding. It was during the Boer War in South Africa that he envisaged young people learning how to 'Be Prepared'.

'Boer' comes from the Dutch word for farmer, the Boers being descendants of Dutch farmers who had settled there in the 17th Century. These farmers were followed by British settlers who moved into the region. During the ensuing 200 years these rival groups competed for the land and the valuable mining rights as the area was rich in gold and diamonds. Eventually hostilities came to a head and the disputes got more bitter. Whilst British and Boer politicians tried to reach a settlement, Baden-Powell's regiment, the 13th Hussars, were asked to keep an eye on the situation and Captain Baden-Powell was sent into the bush to 'scout' ahead and find what the opposition were up to.

He had learned to trap and cook rabbits in the 'out of bounds' woods whilst at Charterhouse School back in England and hide from his pursuers if necessary. Whilst stationed in India he had managed to track down his stolen bike by following the bike tracks left in the dew covered dust. By 1893...............*"I started to teach scouting to young soldiers in my regiment. I wanted to make them feel they were a match for any enemy, able to find their way by stars or by map, accustomed to notice all signs and to read their meanings, and able to fend for themselves away from regimental cooks and barracks............"*
From Baden-Powell's own words during an interview for the Listener magazine in 1937.

This wasn't yet the beginning of scouting as that didn't happen until much later. He wrote a book called 'Aids to Scouting' for soldiers which was very popular. It wasn't until the siege of Mafeking in 1900, when boys were recruited to act as orderlies and messengers, leaving the soldiers to do what they did best. They did such a good job that the idea to write a book about scouting for

boys came into being. First of all though, he had to try it out for real............ *"I got together twenty boys of all sorts, some from Eton or Harrow, some from the East End of London, some country lads and some shop lads and I mixed them up like plums in a pudding to live together in camp."*
From same interview to Listener magazine.

So not only did scouting begin but Baden-Powell can also claim royalties as the person who devised the popular television show, 'Big Brother'! His book, 'Scouting for Boys' was intended as an aid to the YMCA, Boys Brigade and other such societies but shortly afterwards young people wrote to him to say that they'd formed troops and patrols and asked adults to be their leaders. So as Lord Baden-Powell said, "I didn't start the Boy Scout movement, because the blooming thing started itself".

A couple of things of interest before we leave Lord Baden Powell. He was actually Christened Robert Stephenson Smyth Powell, the 'Baden' being added after his father's death. This name came from the same Robert Stephenson who was the railway and civil engineer who just happened to be his godfather. Now, as you know, my grandfather fought in the Boer War and could quite easily have met Baden-Powell. Baden-Powell in turn might have come to Westhoughton when his godfather was building the first railway. So Scouting, which is a world-wide movement could actually have been devised by my grandfather and his mate Robert Baden-Powell whilst they were playing being soldiers/scouts in Hulton Park wood!

The Scout group I belonged to had a 'trek cart', on which we transported all our equipment, tents, pots and pans and all the scouts' rucksacks. The cart was a flat topped, open affair with two handles protruding from the edges and two large wooden wheels. It was a bit like a rickshaw and needed to be pulled by as many scouts that could get to the handles. Great fun at first but after a few hundred yards it became extremely difficult to handle, especially when going uphill and many of the scouts gave up. Skip used to shout orders to the 'worker ants' pulling the contraption as he strolled merrily along telling everyone how great scouting was!

Our uniform was something else! Dark blue shorts made out of a material that itched like mad, khaki coloured shirt and socks which were held up by elastic supports with green edges that protruded from the turn downs but the 'piece de resistance' was the hat! When I say, "We always Get our man!" that might give you a clue. Royal Canadian Mounted Police hats with four dimples in the top and a wide flat and rigid brim was standard equipment, replacing dark green berets. To keep the rim of the hat solid it was necessary to soak the brim in sugared water and then iron it until it was perfectly flat and rigid. However, some of the scouts mustn't have possessed sugar or irons in their homes because they used to look like Jed Clampett from the 'Beverley Hillbillies'. In fact, it became quite an art to see who could have the waviest brim. We learned new words like woggle, toggle, neckerchief, lanyard and we had a troop and several patrols, mine was Hawk Patrol, but the most important think we learned in scouting was to 'be prepared!'

We used to get badges for being proficient in certain pastimes like cooking and...... cooking......and.....I can't think of anything else, so I'll reminisce on cooking. Martin Purtill, Cyril 'Tink' Taylor and myself were given the role as head chefs for a particular evening meal and so the troop went out for the afternoon leaving the three of us to make supper. We decided to make soup which we re-named 'goulash' because it sounded more substantial than plain soup. All the ingredients in the kitchen, including raw bacon, potatoes, carrots, etc. were thrown in a 'Billy' can and left to cook over the open wood fire. I'm not sure who suggested it but it was felt that a special ingredient was needed to make it 'a la' Hawk Patrol. Martin was the son of a pig farmer from Hart Common. (There are beautifully emotive areas in Westhoughton like Hart Common, Daisy Hill, Four gates, Wimberry Hill, Snydale, etc. I do tend to get carried away don't I?) Martin always had a lingering aroma of ammonia from the pigs which didn't help when he was wearing his wellies. Then the flash of inspiration that brought 'Sweaty Wellie Soup' into the world of cookery. We stirred the contents of the pan with Mart's wellies and the resulting mixture was probably worthy of one or two Michelin stars! We, of course, didn't try it but nobody ended up in hospital although several noses kept twitching as they ate. I bet none of us got swine flu! I recently phoned the Swine Flu hotline but couldn't get through for 'crackling'!

Being a farmer's lad 'Mart' was very strong and never knew when to stop working. We were once camping in Silverdale and Skip asked him to dig a latrine. That was a bad mistake because no dimensions for this hole were given. Martin began to dig and everyone forgot about him. Several hours later, Skip was passing by the area where the latrine should have been and came across Mart, at least six or seven feet below him, in a hole that was large enough to house at least twenty of Mr. Purtill's pigs! "When should I stop digging, Skip?" was Martin's plea.

On Easter week-end one year we camped in one of the fields of Martin's farm. We all slept in a massive tent that I'm sure was from the Ark. It was known as a 'bell' tent but looked a bit like an Indian wigwam made from dark green camouflage material. Bloke goes to the doctor and says, "I'm not sure whether I'm a wigwam or a tepee". Doctor replies, "You're too tense (two tents)". It could be mid-day in the height of summer but when you entered through the flap, total darkness hit you, quite frightening really. We woke up on Good Friday morning to a covering of snow and melting snow creating a stream in our tent. In the afternoon it was warm enough for us to go swimming in the stream that we had dammed the day before. English weather, eh? It often confuses me when I'm told that the 21st June is the first day of summer and that the 24th June is Mid-summer's day. That about sums up the English weather, six days for summer if we're lucky! As the forecast for the night was similar to the previous evening it was decided that we would sleep in one of the barns. Much warmer and cosier in the hay but several of our comrades weren't too keen on having the odd rat for sleeping companions!

Eleven

Altar Boy

Besides being in the scouts I was also an altar boy. This meant helping the priest celebrate mass. In those days we had to answer the priest when he was going through the ritual, just like today, except we had to speak in Latin. We didn't know what we were saying but learnt all our responses 'parrot' fashion. I wore a cassock and a surplice, a white garment over the black cassock. We all looked very holy and tried not to laugh when other boys played tricks on us. Not only was I an altar boy at my home church but when school knew this, they asked me to come in early to help their priests celebrate mass. We used to see how quickly a mass could be said. On Sunday's you were talking about an hour but on a Tuesday morning at Thornleigh, I'm sure some of those priests were after breaking the Guinness world record. I think the shortest time was about six or seven minutes!

We were also required to help at weddings and funerals which was no trouble at all because we usually got a tip from the participants; at funerals the tip was usually from a relative rather than the participant!

I regularly attended daily mass to help one of the many priests at school but previous to that I went to my own church most mornings. It must have been noticed in the corridors of power because one year I was asked to join in the May Day processions. Most churches have a "May Queen" but we went a step further. In addition to the 'Queen' we had a 'King' as well. He was named the 'Earl Marshal' and was more ridiculously dressed than the Queen! He wore white satin trousers, white satin shirt with a cloak and white tri-cornered hat with an ostrich plume. He carried a staff which was adorned with lilies and all the old ladies sighed and ah'd and ooh'd whilst all my mates laughed and jeered and called me names for weeks after.

Twelve

Youth Club

Soon after my father died I started attending Westhoughton Youth Club. It had just moved from the Senior Lads school to a purpose built building on 'the houses'. The houses, as they were known, was the council estate to the south of the town. The leaders of the club were Joe and Lil Talbot, an ex-miner and his wife who were to become firm friends. They were ably assisted by May and Arthur. I immediately fell in love with everything it had to offer, table tennis, darts, football and girls! I was at an all boys' school and very rarely had any dealings with the opposite sex. I made loads of new friends both male and female and totally engrossed myself in all the Club had to offer.

It was open every night plus Sunday afternoon and for a very long time I never missed a session. I met Ian Burns who was to become my best friend. We did everything together. He was a very accomplished table tennis player and he spent many nights helping me to hit the ball with my 'back hand' until I could give him a reasonable game. We played darts and table tennis for the club and, on visits to other clubs, would be in the football team as well. We once had a trip to Accrington Youth Club and I played on Accrington Stanley's pitch, what an honour! At night we were entertained by the 'Spinners' but we all sneaked out to the pub as no-one wanted to listen to a 'Folk Group'!

After a while my brother James, or Jim to most people, began to come with me to the club. He could play guitar so he soon became a centre of attraction as we all liked a sing-song occasionally. We were asked to entertain the local pensioners as a good will gesture and Jim was asked to form the musical accompaniment. He enrolled the help of a local guitarist named David Littler who was to become a major part of my life in years to come. When a show took place, Jim liked to wear an all black attire consisting of black trousers shirt and shoes. David, being a keen cricketer was urged to wear his cricketing gear so they became the 'black and white minstrels' and were the entire orchestra! I would sing a song or two, Ian would play mouth organ, Willy, Terence and Tony Thompson would do a funny sketch and Linda and Christine would be the feminine attraction of our shows! We were soon to be joined by another person who became a lifelong friend. John Fearnley, stage name 'Johnny Lee' was the local magician and all round 'good egg'. He had everyone in stitches with his Tommy Cooper-esque magic tricks and world famous singing impressions!

We even gave ourselves a name that has been subsequently purloined by another Westhoughton group of entertainers. We called ourselves W.A.V.E.S. which was the Westhoughton Amateur Variety Entertainment Society and loved every second of being 'entertainers'.

We'd rehearse in one of the rooms off the main hall in the Youth Club and have amazing nights of song and humour. John loved 'show business' so much he would regularly accompany myself and Jim home, even though he lived near the Youth Club, so that he could talk about his greatest love. We'd walk and talk show business each night and call at the chippy where John always had pudding, chips, fish, peas and gravy. By the time we got to our house it was getting very late but just enough time for John to call at another chippy to have two fish and chips to eat on the way home. Amazingly, after several years of this, John began to put on a bit of weight. After several months we saw that the weight was beginning to disappear. "I've decided to go on a diet", he said. "I've stopped having supper," was the key to his weight loss!

Thirteen

Football

I played football to a reasonably high level and together with a friend, Gerald Seddon, was signed on by Wigan Athletic as members of their youth section. At the time the 'Latics' were in the Northern Premier League and played their home games at Springfield Park. We had to go into a room in the clubhouse with several officials looking on as we signed our registration. As I didn't have much self confidence, after a while I didn't think I could ever make it to the professional ranks, so came home to Westhoughton to play in the local leagues there. Don't forget, I had no male role model any more to help guide me on my way and things were altogether different in those days. Training was advisable but not particularly imperative and I got no great encouragement from anyone.

It didn't matter because I played with the legendary Riley brothers from Chequerbent. Keith, Brian and Kevin were from a footballing dynasty. Their mother was well known locally and at one point ran a team in the Bolton League. They were known as Riley's X1 and everyone in the league feared them. Mrs. Riley was eventually banned from running a football team because she was constantly in trouble from the authorities for swearing at officials. Tommy Gorringe played with them as did Gordon Morris, known locally as the 'White Pearl' after the great Pele who was the 'Black Pearl'. When they played on Chequerbent's pitch, which was quite narrow, any opposition team readily gave them a corner rather than a throw in. Keith, who played centre half, could drop the ball directly onto his brother Brian's head with pinpoint accuracy. Brian, who played centre forward, would stand on the goal line and threaten the goalkeeper with grievous bodily harm if he attempted to catch the ball. The ball duly arrived and Brian headed it into the net with ease, as Kevin smiled on through his 'Zapata' moustache, brilliant!

Football, as well as many other sports had been played in Westhoughton for many years. They used to have boxing matches on the Red Lion football pitch attended by many hundreds. Walking races were very popular a hundred years ago and up to 5,000 would attend a race meeting. We can boast an 'Olympian' in Ethel Johnson, who competed in the Los Angeles Olympics of 1932, although she did not qualify from her heat due to injury. In that year she had broken the world record for the 100 yards but it was not recognised as the official distance had been changed from yards to metres.

We can boast two footballers who have gained full caps for their country in Jack Bruton and Francis Lee.

Jack played for Burnley and Blackburn whilst 'Franny' graced the field for Bolton, Manchester City and Derby County. I once played in goal against Franny in a charity event and as he sidestepped me and passed the ball into the net, leaving me in a heap, he quietly said, "Tony, stick to singing!" Nicky Hunt who started his career at Bolton has gained 11 caps for the England under 21 team.

Westhoughton Cricket Club is named 'The Tyldesleys' after Bill, Jim, Harry and Dick Tyldesley who all played for Lancashire. The club prides itself on the fact that it has supplied more cricketers to the county than any other club in Lancashire, the most recent being Michael Watkinson, the current manager of his county. The club recently moved home to a bigger ground with wonderful facilities following an offer from Sainsbury's that they couldn't refuse!

Looking through a book from the *Images of England* series, compiled by Ken Beevers (The History Press 2000) who used to be area librarian in Bolton and local historian, I found a picture of Chequerbent football team from the 1922/3 season. They were nicknamed the 'midgets' which is not surprising as they were probably all undernourished (during that time the mining industry in this area was in terminal decline and unemployment reached an amazing 50% in the 30's). They competed in a match with Dobb Brow and after 90 minutes it was a draw. Both teams agreed to play extra time until someone scored – a sort of early 'golden' goal. The game kicked off at 10.30 am. and finally ended at 3.25pm. but unfortunately Ken doesn't tell us who won. I've seen a few matches at the 'Reebok' that would have probably lasted longer given the same rules!

Sport and music in Westhoughton at the turn of the twentieth century was incredibly important and drew tremendous crowds. On the Red Lion football pitch, which is now covered by a McDonalds and small shopping centre including Gee Tee's, there would be boxing tournaments as well as football matches. These could be attended by upwards of 5,000 people. Walking races were extremely popular as was cycling and the town boasted two very good cricket teams (still does!) Gee Tee's is a large store named after its' owner, George Twist, a friend of mine, whose father, of the same name, was a top class football referee. He played amateur football until he was wounded in 1915 and then took up refereeing. Probably his biggest match was the F.A. Cup fourth round tie between Plymouth Argyle and Chelsea in January of 1936. He was a great supporter of local football and was elected to the Lancashire Football Association Council, becoming their longest serving member when he died in 1976. I always remember him in the Red Lion pub. He had his own chair near the bar and woe-betide anyone trying to sit there when he was in the hostelry.

I was far more interested in participating in a game of football rather than watching, so I only began to support my beloved Bolton Wanderers intermittently as a youth. I saw the legendary Nat Lofthouse play, together with Stanley Matthews, Tom Finney, Billy Liddell in a charity match at Burden Park. It was for the physiotherapist at the club and I went with a group of friends from school. Bolton Wanderers of the day were playing legends X1 so Nat Lofthouse, or 'Lofty' as everyone knew him was up against Eddie Hopkinson, another Bolton favourite, in goal. At one point during the match, Stan Matthews received the ball on the wing and chipped a perfect ball for 'Lofty' in the centre circle. Nat jumped to head the ball and missed it by a mile which caused Eddie Hopkinson to fall on the floor in fits of laughter. He was so amused that he couldn't move for laughing as Lofty took the ball at his feet and calmly dribbled it past him and into the net. I was to meet Lofty, in person, many years later but that's another tale.

Once, Bolton were playing West Bromwich Albion in a cup match, at Burnden Park and I had arranged to meet some friends there. I always stood on the 'Embankment' end in those days. The crowds were not segregated so when I arrived early, there was a crowd of about 300 West Brom fans behind the goals. I was standing alone about twenty feet behind them when I was joined by a much younger lad. He had a bottle of pop in one hand and a meat and potato pie in the other. I can still picture the scene; the lad takes a bite out of the pie and makes a groaning noise, spits out the pie and lobs the remainder into the crowd of people some twenty feet below. The pie hits a bloke smack in the middle of his head and sprays over his friends who are on either side of him. He turns round and looks up. I look down and realise that I am alone, the kid's scarpered! I couldn't blame the men at all, as they slowly approached me; I knew I was in trouble. "You'll not believe this, but it wasn't me, I pleaded," to no avail. They very kindly only hit me a few times each, then went back to their position behind the goals.

We once entered a competition through the youth club to play in a five-a-side gala on the pier at Morecambe. There were hundreds of teams and two leagues to cope with the numbers. The youth club had entered two teams in the competition and we were placed in different leagues. The winners of each league were to go forward to play in the All England five-a-side championships at Crystal Palace, London. We had two good teams who reached their respective final. Unfortunately, we both lost but we'd had a great day. We decided to celebrate by having a drink or two at the bar on the pier. Several pints later we emerged onto the promenade and immediately saw Morecambe Bay in front of us. "Let's go for a swim!" came the communal roar. As we'd just played football most of us had our swimming trunks on under our trousers. These were discarded and the intrepid explorers leapt into the Irish Sea. You're thinking we shouldn't have gone swimming after having a few pints. You're probably right but that wasn't where our, or should I say my, problems arose. We finished the swim and Joe Talbot said we needed to be back at the bus in ten minutes. We start climbing out of the sea and onto the promenade which was quite busy with holidaymakers. "Where do we get changed", shouted one of the lads. "Who knows", came the reply. Eventually it was decided that we should form a circle (not everyone went for a swim) and that each of us would enter the circle, dry off and emerge fully clothed. Brilliant idea! Slowly we all started to get change, leaving me last. Dutifully, I entered the circle, took off my trunks and began to dry myself, when all of a sudden everyone disappeared, together with my trunks and the towel. As I had had a few pints I just stood there laughing at their playfulness (buggers!). I'm sure I saw a girl walk past me on more than one occasion!

Morecambe has seen a major decline in tourism over the years. Once a major resort and boasting two piers it now has no piers and tourism has dropped off dramatically. I think it's a really lovely place and deserves far more visitors than it gets. Eric Morecambe's statue has seen the number of visitors rise since it's installation in July 1999.

The Youth club had become part of my life during this period and I stayed on as a member until I reached 20. It's hard to describe a Youth Club to kids today because it was a vibrant, pulsating and wonderfully exiting place to be. Every Wednesday we had a pop group to entertain us. There were over three hundred young people there and the place was buzzing. Some of these groups went on to become professional musicians but they can always say they started at Westhoughton Youth Club!

Fourteen

The Gunfight at the OK Corral

Rivalries took place during this time and the occasional bit of trouble flared. Most of the time Joe and Lil could sort it out but there were times when more down to earth measures were needed. Every now and then a couple of bikers came from Little Hulton to the Wednesday music night. On one visit they had a 'fall out' with a few of the members. They were sent on their way with tail between their legs. That was the end of matters, or so we thought. A couple of Wednesdays later we heard a commotion at the front door of the club and a window was smashed. Everyone piled outside to see what the trouble was. At least thirty motorbikes with leather jacketed riders and their pillion passengers sat revving their bikes whilst swinging spanners, chains or anything else that could frighten the life out of most kids. Joe made Lil stay inside as he went to persuade the bikers to leave. "We're here to smash this place up and everyone in it!" came the retort.

Joe wasn't sure what to do and many of the members were absolutely terrified when all of a sudden, through the crowd of frightened teenagers strode Kenny Young and Roy Moleneux. Both Roy and Ken were from Bolton but loved to come to Westhoughton for a night out. They had been fully accepted by everyone and had become honorary Keaw Yeds. Both were bikers and both could certainly take care of themselves. They strode forward and Ken grabbed the leader of the gang whilst Roy did the same with the biggest member. They proceeded to knock them off their bikes and kick them around a bit. Eventually they let them get back on their bikes and told them to get out of town. A bit like Burt Lancaster and Kirk Douglas as Wyatt Earp and Doc Holliday at the O.K. Corral!

Although we never saw the gang from Little Hulton again at the Youth Club there was a very famous confrontation with a gang from that area in the main streets of Westhoughton. There used to be a disco night for young people at the Reform Club, on Park Road. My brother told me of the night, as he was in town during the fracas. He and John Fearnley had gone for a pint in the White Lion, a pub that's had quite a few mentions so far! The pub is opposite the Reform club which is on the site of the mill that was burned to the ground in 1812. A similar incident occurred as at the Youth Club when some lads had come down to the disco from Salford. They had been sent on their way, only to return a couple of weeks later with about a hundred reinforcements. They had proceeded to walk down Market Street smashing shop windows as they went. Jim and John, sitting quietly in the White Lion, no doubt talking show business, were rudely interrupted when a brick sailed through the window followed by a gang of youths fighting each other; I think they came through the door rather than the window but nothing would surprise me!

The landlord called for the police and several 'paddy wagons' came from all over the district to clear up the mess. Jim recalls that police were arresting youths on the street, but as there were so many, they were handcuffing them to lamp posts until reinforcements arrived. When the disco goers at the Reform club realised what was happening they began to slowly emerge to find their adversaries fastened to the posts. They soon plucked up enough courage to approach them and proceeded to bang their heads into the lampposts. Police, returning to their captives, were surprised that many of them had bleeding noses! Anyone would think that Westhoughton could be described as the Dodge City of the North. That isn't quite true as that title has been reserved by Barnoldswick on the Lancashire/Yorkshire border.

I'd got to the age when I was accepted in pubs, so I'd regularly go to the Youth club, followed by an hour in the 'Bug'. Everyone in Westhoughton knows the Rose Hill Tavern by that name but for many years nobody knew why. I'm told that an American visitor explained the reasoning. He'd apparently lived here at one time then emigrated to the States. He explained that there used to be a Work House on the site of the pub; most work houses weren't very pleasant places and were known as 'Bug' houses. When the work house was demolished and the public house took its place it also took its name. Ian and I would regularly go to the pub when the Youth Club closed and try to polish up our dart throwing capabilities. Ian's father was a very good dart player and once reached the quarter finals of the famous News of the World competition. Although he wasn't a drinking man or a gambler he would spend many hours in the 'Bug', honing his skills. Apparently blokes would come from miles around to challenge him and bookies would take bets on the outcome. Jackie Burns, as he was known, worked at the local factory, Bellhouse Higson. He was mending some apparatus one day when there was an explosion and he was badly burned. He lived for several days but eventually succumbed.

All the blokes in the pub knew Ian's dad and we were taken under their wings. They bought us the occasional pint and taught us the intricacies of the dart board, how to add up and take away, how to improve our overall game. We both became quite proficient and thought that we could join a team in the local league. As several members at the Youth Club played darts to a reasonably high standard it was suggested that we join the Westhoughton darts league so we applied for entry. It caused major repercussions at the annual general meeting as no team had ever entered the league who was not affiliated to a pub. Eventually it was agreed that we could join and the fixtures were drawn up. Our 'home' was the Youth Club but it was agreed that all our players had to be at least eighteen years of age so that when we played 'away' fixtures there would be no problems concerning alcohol.

Matches were played on a Monday night and consisted of five games of 1001. There were five players on each team and all ten played at once, following each other until the score was reached. Each player was handicapped so that things were more even. This was to prevent top players joining the same team in an attempt to 'Cup Hunt'. This meant that a highly handicapped team could play off 1,501 to the other team's 1001. Did you understand all that? If you didn't, it doesn't really matter as it has nothing to do with my next few sentences. Matches started at approximately 8.45 and usually lasted until 'last orders' at 10.20. As the Youth Club only supplied tea, coffee and for the risky, a glass of Vimto, all the other teams absolutely hated playing us. They would arrive at 7.30, start playing immediately and, if they were lucky, could be out of the place by 8.15. We did extremely well in the league and found that lots of teams were after 'poaching' our players. We were to find out that they didn't particularly want us for our playing capabilities but as a means to end the Youth Club's participation in the league through lack of players, so they didn't have to spend another night at the Youth Club!

Once, Joe decided to have a boxing match in one of the side rooms. I don't know if he did this for a specific reason but several of the tough guys thought they could get their own back on other members that they had a problem with. Joe didn't let it go too far until one of the lads challenged him to a round or two. Rather cockily he climbed into the ring to give Joe, who had been retired from work for several years, a good 'seeing to'. Wrong! Joe played around with him for a minute of two then, following a swing by the lad, decided to flatten him. He wasn't as cocky on future meetings.

Fifteen

Southport and Keswick

A gang of lads decided that a weekend away would be good fun. For many weeks to come we would go to Keswick and camp on the manicured lawns adjoining Lake Derwentwater. We spent most of the day walking the fells and the night, as usual, making trips round the pubs of Keswick. We nearly always started and ended in the 'Woolpack'. We absolutely adored and still love the Lake District which is one of England's fifteen National Parks. Not only is it the biggest National Park in England but it contains the highest mountain, Scafell Pike, the deepest lake, Wastwater, the longest lake, Winderemere and the wettest inhabited place, namely Seathwaite in Borrowdale. It hasn't always been like that; back in the early 1700's Daniel Defoe commented that the area was..... *"The wildest, most barren and frightful place that I have passed over in England"*.

It wasn't to be for almost a hundred years before people began to take note of its beauty. Several people had written books about the area but in the early 1800's William Wordsworth published his 'Guide to the Lakes' and he saw it all in a different light. His most famous poem was actually inspired by his sister and some of the lines were written by his wife! His sister Dorothy wrote in the Grasmere Journal following a trip to Glencoyne Bay, Ullswater.......... *'I never saw daffodils so beautiful. They grew among the mossy stones about and about them. Some rested their heads upon the stones as on a pillow for weariness and the rest tossed and reeled and danced and seemed as if they verily laughed with the wind that blew upon them over the lake, they looked so gay ever dancing ever changing....."* And brother William got all the credit!

Besides daffodils, the one thing you will see a lot of in the Lake District, is sheep. It's thought that the Herdwick sheep came over with Norse settlers as early as the 10th century. These hardy creatures don't need dry stone walls to enclose them. They have an incredible ability to 'know' where they are allowed to go and will not stray beyond these confines. This is known as being 'heafed' or 'hefted' and they can pass on this amazing skill to their off-springs so that generation after generation will stay on a certain 'fell'. When the 'foot and mouth' disease ravaged the area in the early 21st Century and many herds were culled it was thought that this sixth sense would be lost. To help the 'new' sheep to gain this ability they needed a 'little help from their friends' and electric fences were discreetly hidden, by the farmers, on the fells so as to keep the sheep from straying.

One beautiful day we decided that a rowing boat trip on Derwentwater would be a good idea. One of the gang was nicknamed 'Deest', an unusual name to say the least. The lads that had known him longest explained that Stephen, his real name, was probably the worst footballer in the world and so they decided to call him after one of the world's greatest, Alfredo Di Stefano, who played for Real Madrid and Spain, although as an international he also represented Argentina and Columbia. Di Stefano got quickly shortened to 'Deest'.

We went down to the lakeside, hired a couple of boats between us all and began to re-enact the Oxford and Cambridge boat race. Eventually, we made it to the middle of the lake and began stripping for a swim. Everyone took to the water and had a quick dip. As you would imagine the water was absolutely freezing and bodies began rapidly to refill the boats. 'Deest', who wore glasses, appeared at the surface and passed his watch to someone in the boat. "It's not waterproof", he said and proceeded to return to the lake. Someone shouted, "Deest, you've still got your glasses on!" but he didn't hear. When he resurfaced, without his glasses, he grabbed the side of the rowing boat to pull himself up and whoever was holding his watch dropped it in the lake. Now, Lake Derwentwater is approximately 3 miles long and a mile wide; it has an average depth of 72 feet, or 22 metres which is about ten times the deep end of the swimming pool. He tried to dive down to get either his glasses or his watch without any success whatsoever.

Deest wasn't too happy about the incident and went into an amazing sulk that was to last several days. We arrived at the lakeside and disembarked, looked around and Deest had disappeared. When we got back to our campsite he was nowhere to be seen until someone spotted him in the branches of an oak tree near our tent. When it was time to go out at night, we washed and changed and looked up the tree for Deest. He'd gone! When we arrived at the Woolpack he was sitting at the bar and refused to speak to anyone. We sat down and looked towards the bar; he'd gone! Next pub, he was leaving as we arrived, and when it was time to go back to our tent we found him up the tree! He must have come down at some point and had a sleep but the following morning he was back in the oak tree. This was the ritual for the rest of the weekend and it was only when we returned home that he spoke to any of us again!

We had some great times in Keswick and I remember watching Anne Jones winning Wimbledon in a pub near Moot Hall but it's the things that went wrong that everybody remembers most. Willy Taylor loved to go fishing, so went to the local tackle shop to buy maggots for his trip. We got home late one night and turned on the torch before we entered our tent, only to find that Willy's maggots had been opened and knocked over everybody's sleeping bags. Not many slept peacefully that night.

Willy's best friend was Terry Roscoe and they were inseparable. One night they decide to put their suits on to go out to the Woolpack, unheard of in this area of Britain. When we got to the pub the landlord refused to serve them so I asked him why? He said that he didn't need a reason but just didn't like the look of them. There must be some lesson to be learned from this as they were by far the best dressed blokes in the pub.

We also did some walking as well! Isn't that what most people go to the Lake District for? It gave me a great love for that part of England and over the years I've made many friends up there. I once read that Threlkeld, near Keswick, was the most haunted village in Britain and as far as I know, my wife has never been near the place!

A couple of the lads, namely Trav and Tony, met their future wives there and are still married to Wendy and Hazel respectively. Eventually, the Camping and Caravan Club of Great Britain bought the campsite that we had grown to love and on a future visit we were refused entry. We had to find somewhere else to camp and eventually we found a home in a farmer's field in Portinscale. But it wasn't the same and after many happy times in Keswick we decided to go elsewhere.

Southport was the unlucky recipient of the 'mob' from Westhoughton. We arrived on a Friday evening and pitched our tent wherever there was a patch of grass, usually outside the open air swimming pool. On several occasions we were asked to leave by people who thought it unsightly to have a gang of young lads messing up their park! We were quite a harmless lot but I can quite understand, in hindsight, that a group of young blokes could be quite intimidating.

We'd spend the day playing football on the lawns or go for a swim in the open air pool. The water was always sub-zero so we never stayed long. We didn't usually go for a swim in the sea because the bloke who knows where the sea is wasn't usually around! In the evenings we'd go to the pubs in town. Once, in the Ship Inn, around twenty blokes arrived en masse one night and seemed to take over the pub. They were from a local rugby club and were already sozzled when they arrived. One of the bigger blokes walked up to our table and proceeded to drink my pint. Now I'm a placid sort of a guy but when it comes to my beer, well I'm quite precious about it. It's been said that if I ever spill any, I'm usually underneath it with my mouth before it hits the floor! So rather than let it go I confront the guy.

"Do you realise you've just drunk my ale pal!" I said.

"Oh, I'm sorry!" he says, obviously not meaning it. He then stands up and shouts to all his mates, "I've drunk this guys beer, what should I do?"

I am now beginning to get worried 'cos there's a lot more of them than us and it looks like a fight is on the way.

"Let's have a collection for the guy whose lost his beer", retorts the bloke and proceeds to go round his group with a pint pot, collecting all their loose change.

Things are brightening up and it looks like I'm going to get rewarded here because they are putting far more in the pot than the price of my lost pint. Eventually he returns and asks what my 'tipple' is, goes into the pot, takes out the price of the pint, hands it over to me and puts what's left into his pocket! What a scam! The only thing is, it's his own mates who lose out, not the likes of me who's been the butt of the 'sting'.

All this reminds me of a situation that occurred a few nights ago. I was just nodding off in bed when I heard a loud knock on the front door. I rush down to find a drunk on our doorstep.

"Give me a push mate!" came the slurring retort.

"You're joking; do you know what time it is?"

I returned to bed and just as I was dropping off I was woken by my wife.

"Don't be rotten", she said, "go and give him a push!"

So I got dressed and returned to the front door. The drunk was just leaving.

"Do you still want a push?" I shouted.

"Thanks, pal, the swing is in the garden!"

Sixteen

PHAB

Besides trips to other Youth Clubs, we were invited to attend weekends away with the Lancashire Youth Clubs Association. Originally these short holidays were held in St. Anne's on Sea, near Blackpool. These were the holidays that I'd never had as a child and I loved every minute. They once held the first, of what was to become an annual, talent contest. My brother Jim entered, together with Ian Burns, Tony Thompson, Terence and Willy and myself. I don't think we would have got too far on the X-Factor but we did have loads of fun. On one of these particular weekends we were invited to join one of several talks about the further work of Lancashire Youth Clubs. I joined a bloke named George 'Pop' Morgan who was the organising Secretary's Dad. He was to become a very close friend as was his son, Peter.

'Pop' was talking about the week-long holidays that were available through the P.H.A.B. organisation. **P.H.A.B.** stands for **PH**ysically disabled and **A**ble

Bodied. The basic aim of this organisation was to use it's influence throughout society so that eventually it would no longer be necessary. This is where a group of young people, both able and less able, get together for a week to share experiences. I decided that I would take a week's holiday to act as a Good Samaritan. How wrong I was! I had the best holiday I'd ever had and became involved in a life changing experience that would, to a certain extent, become part of my life.

My first week away was in a place called Singleton Hall, near Blackpool. We met in the main hall and Peter Morgan introduced everyone. He had an amazing memory and remembered everybody's name. I think Sue and her future husband, Joe were the only ones from Westhoughton so I had to get to know people. My first recollection was at the meal table where I was asked to feed Audrey. That wasn't a problem but after I'd fed her, I had to watch other people being fed, which made me feel quite sickly. I thought, "What have I let myself in for?" That was the only time I had any thought of being out of my depth. I made friends during that week who are still great mates to this day.

A week on P.H.A.B. would consist of a structured week where everyone was expected to join in. We'd probably do a show to an invited audience at the end of the week. Productions include 'My Fair Lady', 'The Boyfriend' and lots of other musical extravaganzas. There would be a couple of trips out and maybe a night in with entertainment being provided; otherwise we entertained ourselves and what a time we had. We nearly always had a day in Blackpool, with lunch at the Queens

Hotel, an afternoon on the Pleasure Beach and a night at one of the major summer shows at either the Winter Gardens or the ABC Theatre across the road. Everything was subsidised by different Organisations like Rotary, Queensdeans Association and members of these organisations would join in the fun. Another day trip would be to the Lake District with a trip on the Windermere ferry followed by lunch at the fabulous Rothay Manor Hotel in Ambleside.

What we got up to during these week's would have us before the courts nowadays with Health and Safety. The building at Singleton was a special school for disabled students and because of it had all the adaptations necessary for everyone's comfort. Following a couple of years at this venue, Lancashire Youth Clubs purchased Borwick Hall near Carnforth. This was a building mentioned in the Domesday Book and at that time was a Pele tower built as a defence against the marauding Scots. A Pele tower is basically four walls of approximately twelve feet thick with no entrances, rising to about thirty feet. If there was news of a forthcoming attack, the owner of the building would hoist all his animals up and over the turrets and leave them in the base of the tower. Next would come the food and the family, who would enter the tower and set up home above the animals in the base. Doesn't sound particularly inviting but the walls kept the intruders out and the heat from the animals would give off enough heat to keep you warm. Once the invaders realised they weren't going to get anything they would leave and you could come out of your hidey hole. Borwick was extended in the 15th century and became the stately home of a woollen merchant.

Over the ensuing centuries it was used as a family home, a private members club, a billet for soldiers during the war and prior to being a training centre for young people it was again a family home. It was bought by Lancashire Youth Clubs in 1970 to be used by the young people of Lancashire and beyond as a residential training centre. An offshoot of the Lancashire Youth Clubs Association (LYCA) was P.H.A.B. On the first week after its purchase I spent a weekend emptying rooms of the accumulated clutter of centuries. It was all piled in the 'baronial' hall to be either binned or sold on. In hindsight I think I'd liked to have had Arthur Negus at my side to give me some idea of what I was throwing away!

Many happy memories flood the mind when I recall the happy times I spent in this dear old building. No adaptation for the disabled were in evidence because of the age of the place, so everyone had to make do and mend. You soon made friends as everyone had to be literally 'hands on'. Spiral staircases had to be surmounted if one expected to go to bed, not that everyone did! Even the most independent person required some help in getting round the building.

Some of the biggest wheelchair bound males were extremely heavy and so the ground floor 'smoke room' was used as a bedroom during P.H.A.B. weeks. An able bodied male usually slept in the same room just in case anyone needed help of any sort. We all took turns since you usually got very little sleep when you were on duty. I never really had any difficulty sleeping so I was commissioned more regularly than most to this task. It wasn't a task though, we were all friends together and spent half the night talking. The one thing that most people missed on these weeks was sleep.........working hard all day, drinking most of the evening and talking through the night, so it was bound to happen eventually.

"Tony, do you mind doing the smoke room tonight?"

"No problem but you'll have to wake me up in the morning"

"See you then!"

I make sure everyone's alright, have a chat for a while then it's sleep time. I never need rocking and once my head hits the pillow I'm gone. Unbeknown to me a plan has been hatched. Once I'm asleep the SAS appear and silently lift my bed, with me in it and carry the whole caboodle through the baronial hall, down the stairs, round the bend, through the dining room and into the kitchen, placing the bed on top of the central work area.

I don't possess any pyjamas as I like to sleep uncluttered so I awake several hours later to the smell of bacon and eggs. Still half asleep I begin thinking I must be very hungry as the smell only seems inches away. I stand up in bed and have a stretch only to see half a dozen kitchen staff preparing breakfast round my bed!

Borwick was a happy place because everyone was involved as part of a larger family. Young people, organisers, kitchen staff, gardeners and anyone else you could mention all seemed part of a little Utopia on the edge of Lancashire. Freddie Lutz was gardener and handyman at Borwick and was loved by everyone who met him. He was a German prisoner of War and loved England so much he decided to stay. He became tutor during P.H.A.B. courses and showed everyone how to make beautiful musical boxes. I still have one in my bedroom.

In 1946, more than 400,000 prisoners-of-war were still being held in Britain, in contravention of the Geneva Convention, Clement Atlee's government was in no hurry to release them. It is estimated that a fifth of all farm workers were prisoners-of-war and they were used as labourers on the roads. By 1947 most had been repatriated but an estimated 24,000 had decided to stay. One of the most famous was probably Bert Trautmann who became Manchester City's goalkeeper and famously broke his neck in the F.A. Cup Final of 1956 at the feet of Birmingham City's Peter Murphy. Trautmann played the final seventeen minutes, making crucial saves to protect City's winning score-line of 3-1. He was later to receive the O.B.E. for promoting Anglo-German understanding through football. I didn't know that there was an Anglo German understanding when it came to football? The comedian Stan Boardman always states that the only thing in Manchester City's trophy cabinet is Bert Trautmann's helmet!

On one particular holiday I remember spending the afternoon with Lord Lilford, who had invited us to his house and given us the use of his open air swimming pool and gardens. There was a free bar and lunch was served by the comedians Harry Worth and Jack Douglas. We had a great afternoon and during a tour of the garage (he had about 10 very special vintage and not so vintage cars), I overheard him speaking to Peter Morgan and Lady Lilford.

"Have you got your cheque-book dwaling?"

"No dwaling, have you not got yours?"

"No dwaling. Don't worry, Peter, I'll put a donation in the post."

Several mornings later, at breakfast, Pop Morgan stood up and told us all the Lord Lilford had sent a donation of £10,000.00 through the post. An incredible amount of money from someone who was nearly a stranger. He must have either seen the pioneering work that was going on at Borwick, or he had much more money than sense!

Seventeen

Holiday Jobs

I never had a paper round as a kid so had never experienced work of any kind until after my dad died. My first summer job was at a Weaving Mill in Horwich (I was later to become the only 'weaver' that had worked in a weaving shed!) I was just a labourer moving massive rolls of cloth around the factory together with the loading and unloading of wagons. Fairly mundane work which didn't need much brain power. Two recollections spring to mind when I think of this time. Before I started work it was a well known fact at school that I didn't swear or use foul language. Following six or seven weeks at Victoria Mill and my vocabulary took a nose-dive!

At the end of a days' work the hooter would sound and everyone ran to the exit through a massive steel gate at the front of the factory. These gates were closed at the beginning of the day and only opened at the end so the only way out of the place was through security. One of the staff had been caught pilfering and the management decided they would make an example of him. All the employees were asked to leave their work stations and gather in the courtyard. The thief in question was marched to the front gates by the managing director. As the gates slowly opened our 'criminal' was ceremoniously kicked up the backside and out of the factory! I think the unions might have something to say about that nowadays don't you think?

Just down the road from the mill is the British Aerospace factory, once known as Hawker Siddeley and De Havilland, where both my parents had worked and during one summer I was employed in the Despatch department. Many hundreds worked in the factory and it was well known that people skived off work. It was said that if you walked around the factory for two minutes you would be stopped and questioned as to your destination. If however, you had a piece of paper in your hand, you could walk around the factory all day and nobody would take a blind bit of notice of you!

Not only did I work at the factory I was also a member of their football team. Once a year, all the Hawker Siddeley factories got together for a sporting weekend to help with workforce morale. They played everything from table tennis and darts to basketball, rounders and rugby. Only employees of the company were allowed on this trip so, as I was a short term member of staff, I accompanied them. Lots of the teams were made up purely for the weekend so weren't brilliant but our football team played at quite a high standard. We were therefore made strong favourites for the competition which took place in Welwyn Garden City in Hertfordshire.

We left the factory in Lostock early on Friday morning so got a paid day off work. On arrival in the early afternoon we played our first match which we won comfortably. Later on, in the evening we had our second round match which again was an easy victory. So two more rounds and the cup was ours – easy!

"Let's have a drink to celebrate!"

"Do you not think it might be better if we left off the booze 'til after we've won?"

"Don't worry, we've only got Chester tomorrow and they'll be easy"

"OK, you've twisted my arm!"

We woke the following morning feeling like death, or as Groucho Marx once quoted "He's so full of alcohol, if you put a lighted wick in his mouth he'd burn for three days!"

The team from Chester however, had been banned from the bar on the previous evening and so annihilated us. We were running after four or five balls and everyone we kicked was always the wrong one.

Hawker Siddeley built aeroplanes and was responsible for the building, together with the French, of Concord. On one eventful day, two guys were working underneath the magnificent machine when one of them found that there was a drip coming from the fuselage. He placed a bucket under the leak and carried on working. At the end of the day he poured the resultant liquid into a couple of bottles and handed one to his friend. Once at home he sat looking at the vial, wondering what it tasted like. He took a couple of sips which tasted quite pleasant so decided to finish the bottle.

During the night he got quite restless and went to the bathroom to freshen up. Looking in the mirror he noticed that his nose had started to grow longer. Just then the phone rang, "Billy is that you?"

"Yes, are you alright"

"Not particularly. Did you drink any of that fuel?"

"Yeah, why?"

"Well my nose has started to grow and I feel quite strange."

"Don't worry, but whatever you do, don't break wind!"

"Why on earth not!"

"Because I'm phoning from Abu Dhabi!"

Eighteen

Churchill

Around this time 350 million people worldwide were reported to have seen the funeral of Winston Churchill on television. In 2002 he won the title of 'Greatest ever Briton' in front of Princess Diana, Isambard Kingdom Brunel, William Shakespeare and John Lennon. Nat Lofthouse wasn't even mentioned! I remember my father talking at length about him but certainly not in the same light. Everyone knows that Churchill led us to victory in the Second World War but my dad saw him in a different light. He always said, "He's not bloody liked in Lancashire."

"Why not, dad?" came my reply.

"Look it up in a book!"

So I did!

During the First World War, Churchill, as First Lord of the Admiralty, put forward plans for a naval attack on the Dardanelles to open up a passage through Turkey to Russia. Following a bombardment from naval forces it was thought that everything was going to be easy. The ships then began their assault through the narrowest point of the Dardanelles. Many ships were sunk by mines so it was felt that the infantry would join the ANZAC (Australia and New Zealand Army Corp) forces already stationed there. This caused a delay of 6 weeks giving the Turkish forces time to prepare for the assault.

What followed can only be described as horrendous. At 'W' Beach, thereafter known as the 'Lancashire Landing' the forces of both sides were annihilated. The 1st Lancashire Fusiliers gained six Victoria Crosses 'before breakfast' but ultimately lost six hundred men from a total strength of one thousand. In August of that year the Australian forces also won six V.C.'s at the battle of the Lone Pine. The Lone Pine was the name given to the beach after all the trees were removed to cover Turkish trenches leaving one survivor. Cones from that tree were taken back to Australia by a couple of soldiers and were eventually planted at the shrine of Remembrance in Victoria.

This terrible loss of life did not limit itself to the Lancashire Fusiliers. Of one thousand and twelve members of the Dublin Fusiliers who landed in Turkey, only eleven returned home. All members of the 57th Turkish Infantry regiment were killed in action and, as a sign of respect, there is no 57th Regiment in the modern Turkish army.

Now I can understand what my dad was saying! His father (my paternal grandfather) was a member of the Lancashire Fusiliers during that very same campaign. He had already served for twelve years in the Coldstream Guards and left in 1912 after fighting in the Boer war! When the First World War started he was called up again and was assigned to the Lancashire regiment. I didn't know him so I can't relate any of his tales.

Churchill, however, redeemed himself during the Second World War and the population of Britain agreed that, *"Never in the field of human conflict was so much owed by so many to so few"*.

Churchill was also responsible for many other quotes. I'll just try a few of my favourites. All are reputed to have been his but they are not necessarily accurate. I would love to believe them to be true.

Lady Nancy Astor – "If I were your wife, I would put poison in your coffee!"

Churchill – "If I were your husband, I'd drink it!"

Bessie Braddock – "Winston, you are drunk!"

Churchill – "My dear, you are ugly, but in the morning I will be sober!"

Young Man (Seeing Churchill leaving the bathroom without washing his hands)

"At Eton, they taught us to wash our hands after using the toilet"

Churchill – "At Harrow, they taught us not to piss on our hands!"

And finally: "A woman once drove me to drink and I never had the decency to thank her!"

Nineteen

Newquay

During my last school holidays I got a hotel job in Newquay, Cornwall together with a classmate, Bernard Lowe. Bernard's sister had worked down there the previous year and got us the job. We left Manchester on the overnight bus for a 13 hour journey to Cornwall. I felt quite a lot of trepidation as I'd never stayed away from home before. There were several stops on the journey and I was amazed to find that at around Exeter, we had chance of a pint! There was a pub opposite the cafe stop and we both managed to buy the cheapest pint I was to buy in my life, namely one shilling and five pence! Which reminds me of the pub in Yorkshire, that was selling ale at pre-war prices. The landlord couldn't believe that he wasn't selling much alcohol and asked the locals why they weren't buying when it was so reasonable.

"We're waiting for Happy Hour!" came the reply!

On arrival, we were introduced to the staff. There was a husband and wife who owned the hotel and his father who was the chef. There were three female staff who shared duties as cleaners and waitresses. The girls lived in a caravan in the hotel car park. The hotel was residential but had a cafe that was open to the general public.

It was explained to Bernard and I that local bye-laws forbade the placing of caravans together unless it was a registered site. We were therefore marched about a quarter of a mile down a country lane. Once at our destination we had to climb a gate to find our caravan, surrounded by barbed wire, in the middle of a farmer's field! In the field were six or seven cows, two horses and a flock of geese. Within the compound were two dustbins and the caravan with approximately six feet of protection.

"Settle in boys and we'll see you at 6.30 in the morning."

That was it! We were stuck here for at least eight weeks, how on earth were we going to manage? I was already feeling homesick. We sat in the caravan for a couple of hours and then decided it was time to escape from our prison to find out what the place had to offer, in other words, where was the nearest pub!

We found a campsite farther down our country lane and explained our predicament. As long as we told everyone that used our restaurant that there was a caravan site with nightclub and bars just down the road, we could use their facilities whenever we wanted to. That sorted, we decided to get down to the business at hand; drinking lots of beer, or to be more precise, scrumpy cider (when in Rome etc....)

Several hours later it was time to return to our little 'Alcatraz'. We arrive at the gate and try to get into the field but are confronted by several hissing geese! It doesn't look like we will get any sleep because we'll not get near our caravan!

"Have you anything to feed them with?" asks Bernard.

"I've a packet of Polo in my pocket. Will they do?"

"Anything will do as long as we can get to our van!"

We try with a couple of mints but we throw them too far and the geese aren't fooled. Finally, with the last two mints, we get them to run down the field in pursuit.

"Run as fast as you can!"

We make a dash and get into the compound with only a few gashes in our jeans from the barbed wire. Settling down in our van we both think, "What have we let ourselves in for?"

After a quick wash in cold water we have to go through the whole rigmarole again in order to get out of the field.

We report for duty and are told that we have to do all the washing and preparation of all the vegetables. It doesn't take long before we decide that I will do all the veg. and Bernard will do all the washing after I break several plates and Bernard can't use a peeler! The boss, whose name I can't remember, was a bully, as was his dad and we soon got to do as we were told. We'd been used to bullies for the last six years at school

We settled into a routine which was quite enjoyable; work from early morning 'til about one o'clock; afternoon on the beach trying to get a tan and ogle the bathing beauties; work from about five o'clock. until around eight o'clock then down to the caravan club. We'd return back to our caravan at around midnight armed with several slices of bread that we purloined from the kitchens to satisfy our feathered friends (we weren't going to be caught out twice!) We'd listen to Radio Caroline from then 'til we fell asleep.

Radio Caroline was not the first but was probably the most famous of the pirate radio stations of the 60's. M.V. Frederica, renamed Caroline (supposedly after the daughter of J.F.Kennedy) began broadcasting at Easter 1964. She was later to become Caroline North and move to the Isle of Man. She was replaced in the south by M.V.Amigo and broadcast to the continent and Southern England. On the 14th August 1967, following the recent Marine Broadcasting Offences Act, the station was deemed totally illegal and was ordered to stop broadcasting. We sat listening on our radio late that night, wondering what might happen. On the stroke of midnight the station played the National Anthem followed by Pete

Seeger singing 'We shall Overcome', then the Beatles 'All you need is Love' and carried on as before!

One morning we were wakened by the caravan rolling from side to side. We nearly fell out of our beds as the whole van shook violently. What's going on we thought, only to see one of the cows rubbing its back on the side of the caravan. It had somehow got through the barbed wire and decided it looked like a very good scratching post! We managed to shoo it away and replace our wire fortification.

One afternoon we arrived for work only to be confronted by the 'Gordon Ramsey' wielding one of his machetes.

"If you don't clean up that mess in your field you'll be on the first bus home. How dare you clutter up that field like you've done!"

We'd absolutely no idea what he was talking about so when we returned to our own little field we were surprised to find litter scattered all over the enclosure. The field was at least a couple of acres so it took a while to clean all the rubbish and re-fill our bin. Once done we returned to work to tell 'Gordon' of our efforts. He returned with his son to check our field, which was again covered in rubbish.

"I thought you said you'd cleaned the rubbish. It doesn't look like you've done very much!"

"But we moved every little thing!", we pleaded.

"If it's not clear by tomorrow you are going home!"

We'd, by this time, got used to being in Newquay and we were both enjoying our stay.

"It must be somebody else!" pleads Bernard.

"Don't be stupid!" replies 'Gordon', "just clear it up!"

They left and we spent the rest of the evening cleaning up the field. The following morning we were wakened by a cry from 'Gordon'.

"Get your bags packed and get out of here!"

"But we've cleaned it up three times!"

"No arguments, just leave!"

We stick our heads out of the caravan to find that, sure enough, the rubbish is scattered around the field.

We returned to our caravan with tails between our legs and started to pack our bags, unable to understand what had happened. Suddenly we hear a whinny and one of the horses appears at the window of our van. It proceeds to lift off the dustbin lid with its teeth and proceeds to rummage through the litter trying to find a tasty treat or two! As it pokes around in the bin, piles of debris are scattered to the four winds as 'Gordon' and his son look on!

Reprieved! We did say it wasn't us!

1967 was known as the 'Summer of Love' and its spiritual home was the Haight Ashbury area of San Francisco, even though 'flower power' originated down the road in Berkeley, California. It was 'born' to symbolise the passive resistance towards the Vietnam War. The term 'flower power' was coined by American poet Allen Ginsberg in 1965 and led to a world full of 'hippies' and 'flower children'. The epicentre in Britain was here in Newquay and we would regularly confront people lying in the middle of the road, holding a bunch of flowers or handing out flowers 'willy-nilly' to anyone who would accept them. I'm not sure how they would fare handing out flowers in Bolton town centre?

Twenty

Waiter

On my return home I got a job at my 'local', waiting on
the customers at the Rose Hill Tavern. In those days
every pub had waiters and waitresses. I had to wear a
white shirt with 'dickie-bow' and was supplied with a
cummerbund and fitted white jacket. At weekends the
'music room' opened and entertainment was supplied by
Tommy on drums and Bill on piano. Very similar to the
karaoke evenings of today, except that the music was
'live' and you needed to know the words to the songs.
People would get up and sing their favourite songs but as
today, nobody wanted to be first up. The landlord, Fred,
asked me to sing a song to get them started and this
probably became the first time I entertained in public.
Once I'd done an item they were queuing up to get
'onstage'. Like today, some were good and some were
amazingly bad, although they just didn't realise it
themselves.

Nearly everyone who came out at weekends were known to us and so we learned everybody's order. One of the older staff, Florrie, had a wonderful scam. Immediately her customers came through the door, she ushered them to a seat and verified their order, "Pint of bitter and a sweet sherry?" for example. She'd go to the bar, get served and pay for the drinks. On return to the customers table she'd add an extra shilling to the bill as insurance. Inevitably, the customer would pass over the money and say, "One for you, Florrie?"

"Oh, thank you! I'll just take a shilling"

So every round made her two shillings which added up to quite a fortune by the time 'last orders' were called.

One night I noticed a couple who were strangers to me, sitting near the bar. They seemed to be having a wonderful time. Lots of drinks, lots of cuddles and a few kisses; love's young dream! After a couple of hours I noticed that the bloke had quietly slipped down his seat and gone right under the table. The woman, however, carried on drinking as if nothing had happened. I felt obliged to say something as I walked over to her, "I don't know if you've noticed, love but your husband has just slipped under the table"

"No, he hasn't", replied the woman, "he's just walked into the pub!"

Twenty One

Christmas Post

I tried a couple of sessions working on the Christmas Post but nothing of particular interest occurred. It was quite a pleasant task, delivering good will messages to people around Westhoughton. We would arrive at the sorting office in town and collect a bulging bag of mail. From there we'd catch a bus to the particular destination we were delivering using bus tokens. The sorting office had the envelopes in exactly the right order so we didn't really need to know the area in question. Once the bag was empty it was back on the bus to Bolton to get another bag of post. We could deliver a maximum of three bags in a day so some areas of town got that many deliveries in a single day; unheard of today!

I remember one Christmas Eve. We arrived in town early to collect our bag. The person in charge said that if we took two bags we didn't need to come back into Bolton, so the quicker we did our round, the earlier we could finish; brilliant strategy. Unfortunately, no one told me that I would meet a gang of mates at around lunch-time, just as I'd emptied my first bag.

"We're going to the White Horse, Tony. Are you coming?"

"Well I could just try one and then finish my round".

I then forgot which 'round' I was finishing, so by the time I'd realised that I still had a full bag of mail to deliver it was about 6pm.! I collected my post and on Christmas Eve, whilst the snow was beginning to fall, I was still delivering mail at 9 o'clock at night. People would come to the door and tell me what a conscientious person I was; not realising that was the opposite to the real truth.

Twenty Two

THE REAL WORLD

As I approached my last summer at school I had absolutely no idea what I would do when I left. I wasn't expecting particularly good results, so University was never really on the agenda. I didn't fancy it anyway; too far away from Westhoughton! Seven years at grammar school was supposed to give me an advantage but they'd only prepared us to become civil servants, bankers, accountants or teachers. So which one should I choose? I know, I'll go and work in a bank, it should be fairly easy.

I've been looking through my old papers recently and I found a letter from Savile Row in London saying that I'd been successful in my application to join the Civil Service. I don't remember anything about it but it makes interesting reading. It states that I have been successful in the competition and that if I would like to be considered for the Diplomatic Service they would check if I was high enough in the order of merit to be invited for interview. Just to think I could have been driving round in an Aston Martin as the new James Bond?

I eventually applied for a job with Williams Deacon's bank whose Head Office was in Manchester. Following a successful interview I was offered the princely salary of £475 per annum. The contract was headed 'Male Clerical Staff' which probably meant that females were offered a considerably less amount.

So I'd got a proper job in the real world! I soon found out that my first posting was to be in Pendlebury, near Swinton, Manchester. On the first morning I climbed on the number 38 bus at Wingates only to find Eddie Marsh, my mate from primary and grammar school, sitting in his usual position, at the back of the bus. We exchanged grunts and thus started our new life; it didn't seem much different from the old one! Eddie had got a job working for the same bank but stationed in Walkden, a few bus stops nearer to home.

Banking was considerably different in 1968 than it is today. Everything was done manually; there were no computers to input or access information. Every customer had a 'ledger' which was basically a piece of card about the size of an A3 piece of paper. This 'landscape' (as opposed to portrait) slotted into a frame that housed everyone's account. When a transaction took place at the counter it had to be logged, by hand, on the ledger. First you found the clients' card, wrote out what they'd done (put money in, or taken it out) added all the in's and out's, subtracting the out from the in and leaving a large figure. It had to add up exactly or there were times when we were still looking for the missing penny at ten o'clock at night. Oh, I just mentioned 'penny'; yes it was before decimalisation so we were adding and subtracting pounds, shillings and pence. If you need to know more ask somebody who is very old!

There was no armour plating keeping you away from the customer and the manager sat on a very tall stool surveying all he possessed. It was a bit like Ebenezer Scrooge and Bob Cratchit; me being Bob. There were times he made me feel like 'Tiny Tim'. It was also as formal as the Dickens' way; the manager called me Mister Berry and I had to address him as 'Sir'.

One day a tramp walked into the bank with an old mac tied together with a length of twine, no socks, unshaven and wearing a trilby full of holes. I was about to shoo him away when the manager almost flew from his perch and welcomed him with open arms. When I overheard his name I realised that he was the bank's wealthiest account holder. Obviously a bit, no probably very, very eccentric; he'd come in to see if he could have a few pounds to buy a new pair of glasses and have his false teeth mended! It did re-enforce my dad's view to not take people at 'first impression'.

After I'd got used to the workings of the bank I was used as a deputy around Manchester to cover absentees. I worked in Moss Side where the manager told me not to give money to anybody unless he'd okayed it; talk about stereotypes! One particular week was spent at another branch that will remain nameless. The manager was less formal than my home branch boss so I began to relax. He gave me a guided tour of the branch which ended down a flight of stairs at the vault. Most of the 'safes' required two keys, to be turned at the same time, together with a combination lock and large handle that opens up the vault. Should someone try the keys or the combination at different times the whole mechanism will lock automatically.

"The way to break into this place is easy", says the manager who I've only just met, for the first time.

"You need a car inner-tube, attached to the handle and that pipe up there on the ceiling. Fill the keyholes with explosive and as it blows, the inner-tube will pull up the handle before it locks. By the way, if you can't remember the combination, it's written on the wall over there!" No joke! I was quite amazed at his totally flippant attitude. I wasn't surprised, however, that that particular branch was successfully broken into several years later. I wonder how they worked out what to do?

Although it was quite easy, I was beginning to feel completely out of my depth. I was bored and couldn't see myself as Ebenezer for much longer. One thing I do remember at the time, regarding my salary and where it would go over the years to come. I gave myself an ambition to get my salary up to £1,500 per annum. If I got that much money, I thought, it would be enough to take me through to retirement. I wasn't to realise that decimalisation would have something to say about my ambitions!

On the 15th February 1971, decimalisation arrived in Britain and instead of having 240 pennies to the pound we had only 100! Older people hated the change and most people felt that prices rose must faster because of it. I'm sure that a lot of shopkeepers tried to make a little extra during everyone's confusion but inflation at the time was very high, which added to the bewilderment.

On return to my branch at Pendlebury (by the way, I had to walk past L.S.Lowry's house every morning on my way there) I was surprised to find that we'd got a new assistant manager. He was a Jehovah's Witness and every lunch time he tried to 'convert' me. I once threatened to put his bible where I shouldn't. One thing that this particular gentleman did for me was to introduce me to The Clancy Brothers folk group. They were appearing at the Odeon in Manchester and he asked if I'd like to go with him. I went on the proviso that Jehovah wouldn't come with him! That understood, we met in town and I began, what was to become, a lifelong love of folk music and the consequent lifestyle that goes with it!

The Clancy brothers and Tommy Makem started their singing careers in America rather than Ireland. Tommy, Bobby and Paddy Clancy had emigrated to the U.S after the war and eventually settled in Greenwich village, New York. They were all actors and founded a small theatre company. To augment their income they did late night shows where they sang song from the 'old country'. When Bobby returned to Ireland they were to be joined by Liam and another Irishman, Tommy Makem. Acting was their first profession but singing gradually began to take over. Following an appearance on the Ed Sullivan show which was watched by an estimated eighty million, they were approached by Columbia records and made an album for them. On the album they were accompanied by banjo player Pete Seeger.

The Clancy's influenced much of the Irish music of today and certainly had a massive impact on the material of an up and coming artist by the name of Robert Zimmerman who was later to change his name to Bob Dylan because of his love for the material of Dylan Thomas.

Twenty Three

College

I worked a year for Williams Deacon's and that was enough! I'd applied successfully for Teacher Training so in the autumn of 1969 I went back to 'school'. Lots of things happened that year. Edward Kennedy, the last of the Kennedy brothers, finds himself in trouble following the death of Mary Jo Kopechne at Chappaquiddick Island. They had left a party together when his car plunged into the water. He failed to report the accident for ten hours, by which time her body had been found. He was sentenced to a two month suspended jail sentence. Two days after this all thoughts were on Neil Armstrong who made....*A small step for man......a giant leap for mankind.*

The Beatles perform there last concert on the roof of the Apple headquarters in London and shortly afterwards John Lennon marries Yoko Ono, but instead of going on honeymoon they hold a 'Bed-In for Peace'. That sounds fine if you like that sort of thing but not in front of a world-wide audience! Whatever turns you on! John Wayne wins his only Oscar in 'True Grit' and Michael Cane utters the unforgettable line...... "You're only supposed to blow the bloody doors off!" in the film 'The Italian Job'.

On the 14th August, a month before I was due to start at college and following three days and two nights of violence in the mainly Catholic Bogside area of Londonderry, troops were sent to Northern Ireland. This was supposed to be a 'limited operation' although the Ireland Republic's Prime Minister called it an 'outrageous interference'.

So I started Hopwood Hall College in Middleton, run by the De la Salle brothers, a Roman Catholic teaching order of brothers. The only difference from the Salesians who taught me at school is that these brothers aren't priests and probably, because I was then nineteen years old, not as violent. I soon realised that the college comprised of students from all over Great Britain but mainly Ireland; almost 70% from Belfast and Derry (certainly not Londonderry!) I was going to study to be a P.E. and Geography teacher although that was at least three, maybe four years off. I'm quite an amiable bloke so to make friends was not too difficult. A few pints and everyone wants to be a friend! The Irish lads also enjoyed a good sing-song so that wasn't a problem. The thing that tickled me is that all my fellow students thought I had a funny accent. That's rich, I'm only about 10 miles from home, lots of people round here talk like this; get used to it!

I'm based in college accommodation at George Street on Cheetham Hill, in a large Victorian terraced house which can take about twenty students. I'm sharing a room with another half dozen blokes who hail from as far afield as Gibraltar (and they think I talk funny?) We sleep and dine here, then a double-decker bus picks us up every morning to take us to Hopwood. As I mentioned earlier, I'm a bit of a 'home-bird' and so I lasted less than a week before I had to go home to mummy! From that day onwards I commuted every day which made me feel much happier although it restricted me from fully participating in college life.

I managed a few nights back at George Street but that was the end of living away from home – my wife would argue that I'm still the same; she's lucky I left my mother! I did however, manage a few trips with the lads from college; did I mention, like school, this was an all male establishment. We went on a day excursion to Blackpool, starting at about ten o'clock from Hopwood Hall. One of the lads had arranged it all. We left Middleton and made our way, slowly towards Bolton and then Belmont (the M61 was started in 1969 and completed the following year). Once in Belmont we decided it was time for a break! Straight into the Black Bull at around eleven o'clock and drinking 'til three o'clock at which time we had a collection for the landlord in the hope that he'd stay open a bit longer. This he did, so by the time we left for Blackpool, at about five o'clock everyone was far too worse for wear from the Guinness!

This was a time that I'd begun to get up and give a party turn or two. I knew a couple of Stanley Holloway monologues and could sing one or two Irish foot-stompers which pleased the Gallic contingent! Following my visit to see the Clancey Brothers, I'd learned all the songs from a couple of their albums. It took me an eternity to learn the words to my first ever song and then it became easier at every sitting to learn more. I eventually had a large repertoire of song words which would come in useful later.

Many people know many songs half way through and lots more know what they think are the right words. I always remember a mate of mine who 'knew' the words to a popular Johnny Cash song. In 'A Boy named Sue' there's a line that goes...... 'At an old saloon on a street of mud, there at a table dealing stud, was the dirty, mangy dog who named me Sue' but he used to sing.... 'At an old saloon on a street of mud, there at a table peeling spuds!'

We sang the afternoon away and left for Blackpool. By the time we arrived, most of the passengers had had a sleep, so were ready for the evening session. We drank 'til the pubs shut and went on to the nightclubs in town and drank there until we were thrown out at about two o'clock in the morning. It is the only time in my life that I think I actually drank myself sober (if such a thing exists). Anyway, I felt perfectly alright, unlike some of my friends! Tough that's me! Or am I?

One day at college, we'd been in the gym all morning and I was feeling particularly fit. As we left, to go for lunch, I noticed a large vehicle parked down the side of the building with a banner whose caption read, 'Give Blood'. I'd never given blood before, so I genuinely thought I should try to help others. Now should I go before lunch or after? I'll go in, give blood and I'll be having dinner within the hour. Wrong!

A nurse introduced herself and explained what was about to happen. She'll put a tourniquet round my bicep, insert a needle into the vein, couple of minutes to drain the arm, cup of tea and 'bob's your uncle'! So she took an 'armful' and sat me down with a cuppa and biscuit. Now that wasn't a problem was it? I was just about to take another sip when I came over all lightheaded and woozy. Just as I began to 'go', I had the presence of mind to pass my cup and saucer to someone sitting near me. When I woke up the nurse had me lying on a bed with my feet raised up.

"You were just feeling dizzy, so we've taken this precaution", she assures me. "Have you given blood before?"

"No", came my reply.

"What about having lunch?"

"No".

"Try another drink before you go for your lunch. You'll be OK in a minute".

So here we go again! Trying to take a sip and I'm down again! This time she leaves me for an hour before trying to give me a drink, without much success. Eventually she sends to the canteen for a bowl of soup which she proceeds to 'spoon feed' me.

"You're a P.E. student then?" she passes the time of day, whilst altering my notes..... Do not take blood from this wimp again!

"So you'll be very fit and strong, eh?"

Sarcastic bugger, I can't help being a coward. Eventually they take me to the canteen in a wheelchair and give me lunch. Once I've dined they take me back to their mobile 'torture chamber' to let me recover. By this time, the sun is beginning to set and the nurses are wanting to pack up and go home. They enquire if there's anyone around who could help me. In due course an old school friend arrives as an escort to accompany me to the railway station and onward to Westhoughton via Bolton. What a day! I gave blood at twelve and eventually left the campus at seven o'clock. They probably flushed my blood down a drain on the way back to the hospital, in case it had a 'cowardly' gene that has yet to be discovered!

To convince myself that the previous sentence is true, I only need to remind myself of an instance that occurred not long after this incident. I love most sports and am quite capable in most of the ones that I've participated in. As a P.E. teacher I would need to know the in's and out's of most sports, so we participated in all the popular games to get to know the rules and learn some teamwork amongst our peers. When it came to rugby however, we used the 'union' model, as opposed to the 'league' type that is popular in this part of the world. I'd never played either code as it means lots of physical violence. It's played with a funny shaped ball and, although I love to watch either code on T.V. I'm not too keen on participating in the brutality.

Anyway, we are on the pitch and the referee, who's also our tutor, tells me to tackle anybody with a ball. As soon as the game starts I see a friend of mine powering towards me. He's called Liam Longbottom, comical name don't you think? No you're wrong! there's nothing comical about a 6'7", sixteen stone bloke who wants to break your nose. So I close my eyes and tackle him round the shins. I'm lying in the mud when I feel a tap on the shoulder.

"Alright, Tony? good job it's not a real game, 'cos I'd probably have stood on your head by now!" He smiled and ran off. It was a good thing that there was a lot of mud around!

Whilst I was at De la Salle, I celebrated my 21st birthday. I decided that I would have the 'do' at the Windmill, which was near where I lived. I worked behind the bar there at weekends so it seemed the ideal place. At the time, all the pubs had replaced the hand pump with fiddling glass tubes which measured out a half pint. It had a valve which moved from one end of the tube to the other. The idea was that it gave an exact measure so that nobody could complain about being 'short changed'. It was only later that people realised they could be fiddled with and not only would you get a short measure occasionally, it was guaranteed you'd get one every time. The whole point of that little lot was to explain that the only way they would work is by the means of electricity.

My birthday was in January and in the world outside things weren't looking good. There was an earthquake in China, an avalanche in Val d'Isere, a train crash in Argentina and a power cut in Westhoughton! I arrived at the Windmill for the biggest party of my life and we couldn't get any ale! All my friends arrived from College, together with my mates from Westhoughton, arriving to, as the song goes..............

"There's nothing so lonesome, so morbid or drear, than to stand at the bar, of a pub with no beer!"

What can we do? Stuart, the landlord, thinks he'll have to do something. He's got fifty or sixty young blokes who want to empty his barrels and fill his pockets! Think! If electricity can't be used, then what about gravity? So he goes down to the cellar with a few rugby players, picks up a barrel and empties it into buckets. He then brings the buckets of beer upstairs and the waiting staff just fill pint pots straight from the container, it's a bit flat but who cares, it's better than Vimto! It finishes up to be an unusual but memorable evening as everyone gets their fair share of albeit very flat beer!

During this time, as mentioned earlier, the troubles in Northern Ireland were accelerating and I remember the day, when walking into the college grounds, one of the accommodation blocks was surrounded by barbed wire and on the roof flying proud was the tri-colour flag of the

135

Irish Republic. Within the compound was a blackboard, on which, written in chalk, was a sign stating that this particular block had made a unilateral declaration from the English Government and anyone entering without permission would be treated severely!

"What on earth is going on", I said to myself. "There are mates of mine living in that block and I would be terrified for my own safety if I entered!" It was at that moment that I decided it was time to call it a day. I was becoming more disillusioned with everything that went on at college and wasn't really sure I wanted to become a teacher anyway. I turned round and walked all the way home (about 20 miles!)

Twenty Three

Building Site

Throughout my stay at college I'd been lucky enough to get a holiday job through my brother-in-law. Fred was a building site engineer and every time we had a break he was able to get me a job with his firm. I'd work as brew lad, hod-carrier and general labourer. The work was hard but I loved it; apart from the job I do today, it was probably the most enjoyable employment of my life.

We were working on a "Refuse Incinerator" just outside Altrincham. Fred would pick me up every morning and I would sleep all the way to work! On my first day I was given the job of brew lad. I'd walk around the site and take orders for the morning and lunch time breaks. The site was several miles from town so someone took me into Altrincham and I returned with butties, pies or chips. Before I left I had to make sure the boiler was filled and turned on and that all the cups and plates were washed. All the crockery was absolutely disgusting so I made the mistake of cleaning it all using sand as an abrasive. When the blokes came into the cabin at 'brew' time no-one recognised their own cups because they were so clean.

It was a massive site and the whole building was made from concrete. The joiners would make shuttering from timber, which was basically a mould into which the concrete would be poured. These moulds would be filled with metal reinforcements onto which the concrete was poured. Apart from "fancy" bits of moulding, the shutters were going up very rapidly so the concrete wagons were arriving every few minute of the day. Most of this was spread and vibrated by a group of Irish workers who travelled daily from Newcastle-under-Lyme by mini-bus. What a great bunch of fellows they were; one used to greet everyone daily with the phrase, "'Tis a great day for work!"

During break times they'd ask me questions like,

"What's the capital of Lichtenstein?"

"I've no idea," came my reply.

"And you want to be a Geography teacher! No chance!"

During one of the breaks, one of the Irish blokes knocked his coat off the hooks at the back of the door. Out of his pocket fell a dozen or more un-opened wage packets. His mates apologised for him, "Oh, Paddy doesn't need to work. He won a few hundred thousand pounds on the horses a couple of years ago! But what would he do without the craic?" (Craic – pronounced crack, is obviously a Gaelic word with no exact English equivalent. There's an expression 'ceoil agus craic' meaning 'music and fun'. It simply means having a good time or a laugh). Well, work seemed to be a good craic for all of them, they started and ended the day with a smile and every day was greeted by the phrase "'Tis a great day for work!" It could be raining, snowing, freezing, boiling but it was always, "a great day for work!"

So after I'd walked out on college I was allowed to keep my job on the building site. It was great fun and I've never been as fit but it was obvious I didn't want to be a labourer for the rest of my life. Fun when you're younger but the older blokes walked around with lots of limps, hunched shoulders and arthritic hands through year upon year of hard work and toil. They couldn't take six weeks off work if they injured their metatarsals!

All manual workers who dig holes are referred to as 'navvies' although the word was originally used for construction workers on the canals and later the railways. All excavations in Britain were mainly done by hand in the 18th Century and as the canals 'navigated' between the larger towns and cities the workforce were known as the 'navigators' which was eventually shortened to 'navvies'. The canals were built to transport heavy loads from town to town. A single horse could pull a barge full of heavy materials. Before the advent of steam, the canals were the arteries for movement of heavy goods. You might be surprised to know that the city of Birmingham has more miles of canals than Venice!

Which reminds me; there's a bargee who is transporting a boat full of manure from one city to the next. At a lock gate he is approached by a bloke who asks for a lift.

"Not a problem!" cries the bargee, "jump aboard. And what do you do for a living?" inquires the bargee.

"The name's Barrington Forfesque and I'm a thespian! You might like to know that I'm on my way to Manchester to perform in Shakespeare's Midsummer Night's Dream!"

At the next lock, the gate keeper enquires "Bargee, what are you carrying?"

The bargee replies, "A barge full of manure and an actor!"

On several more instances our bargee was asked the nature of his business and what load he was carrying.

The bargee, at every juncture replied, "A barge full of manure and an actor!"

Eventually, Barrington leans over to the bargee and says, "Bargee, would it be possible to discuss the billing?"

Twenty Four

School for Deaf

During all the time at college I had still been spending all my spare time involved with P.H.A.B. either going up to Borwick for the weekend or inviting several of the friends I'd made, back to my home. My mother never knew who to expect. She was absolutely marvellous with them all and they all grew to love her, even though they knew her as the 'Queen Mother'. My only proviso to anyone who visited was that my routine would not change and you therefore did what I did or not bother coming. It was generally OK for most because what I did was go to the pub and that was more than acceptable.

On one particular visit to my home by Emmett, who lived in the 'Spastic Society' home in Buxton (a horrible name that has now been changed to SCOPE as a term to refer to people with cerebral palsy), we were on our way to the pub for a pint and some lunch, when an old lady who knew me, stopped to have a few words.

Without directing a single word to Emmett, she began patting him on the head whilst saying to me,

"Are you taking him to the spastics club, love?"

"No, I reply. By the way, he can understand you."

All the while Emmett is getting more and more annoyed. Whilst it is quite difficult to understand what he is saying, he can be quite 'vocal' at times.

"Bugger off you silly old cow!"

"Eh, you do a wonderful job!", the lady continues talking to me.

"I said bugger off, we're trying to get to the Red Lion!" continues Emmett.

"Is he trying to say something?"

"I will say something if you don't leave us alone! #*+?# off!"

So to get away, I intervene. I pat Emmett on the head and say to the lady, "I think he needs to go to the toilet! Bye bye!"

Attitudes towards disability of any form have changed dramatically since I was younger. Things still need to improve but the changes, brought about by organisations like PHAB, have made life far more bearable for a small percentage of the population.

I see a job advertised a few days later. It's for a housefather in a school for the deaf in Bolton. The school is residential and the job entails looking after a group of boys when they are not at school. I fill in an application and following a successful interview I embark on another episode of my life. In those days it was genuinely possible to leave a job on Friday and start a new one on Monday, or, if you were in a hurry, the day after!

The school was originally built as a residential home for deaf and blind children, so the fire alarms in one side of the building were bells whilst on the opposite side, were flashing lights. I was in charge of around a dozen 12 year old boys. Every night they came home from school, which was just across the playground, and engaged in structured play. We went to the swimming baths twice a week, played football, cricket and basketball, spent some time doing homework, then, after a meal, relaxed and watched telly. What was unusual in itself was that the boys were banned from watching only one television programme, 'Vision On', a series for the deaf! The reason they couldn't watch it was because the presenters used 'sign language', which was banned in school. School policy dictated that students should not sign but 'read' each others' lips. This was so that all the pupils would learn to 'lip read' so that they could communicate with everyone, not just people who could understand sign language. Things have changed more recently and deaf children are treated with a little more dignity. If they choose to sign then it is their prerogative.

Every morning it was my job to wake them all up and get them ready for breakfast. After that, they were off to school and I would tidy up after them, wash any dirty bedding, make the beds, tidy their play areas, etc. Before doing my 'housework' we joined the kids in assembly and it was compulsory to begin and end with a hymn. I think it was Miss Holding who played the piano? She would happily play along whilst about 120 deaf kids sang as loud as they could. What a noise! Never heard anything like it until I recently watched an edition of the X-Factor!

Most of the children came from all over the North West of England and so the majority lived at school. Every weekend they generally went home, so, although we were on duty, we were free to do as we wished. I usually went home, to meet friends and go out for the night. One such weekend I was invited to a 'do' at the Conservative Club. I can't remember what it was but I spent the night with my sister, Anne and her husband, who'd also been invited. She complained about having a headache but it wasn't bad enough for her to go home. At the end of the night we said our goodnights and I went back to school.

The following evening, just as we'd finished our tea, the phone rang. I left the boys watching T.V. and answered the phone. It was my sister, Teresa, informing me that our sister, Anne had died that afternoon. She said that her husband, Kevin, was on his way to pick me up and they would explain everything later. I walked through the hall in a daze and went straight into Denise's room (Denise was another houseparent and a great friend). I explained what the message was and burst into tears. What happened next is only a blur; Kevin arrived and took me home and it was explained that Anne had suffered a cerebral haemorrhage during the afternoon. She'd complained about having a headache, so took the morning off work. Fred, her husband had stayed with her but went to work at lunchtime. When he arrived home she was dead in bed.

You understand when an elderly relative or friend dies but it's always extremely difficult to reconcile the death of a younger person. The whole family were devastated, especially my mother, as a parent always expects to outlive their children. If anything positive can be drawn from this story, it's probably the fact that she had a good life and crammed lots of joy into it. My other sister, Teresa, once lost a baby at 10 days and you can still see the hurt when it is ever mentioned.

After several days had gone by, it was suggested that my brother and I take Fred (our brother-in-law) out to try and cheer him up. One of the funniest acts around is the fabulous 'Oldham Tinkers' and they were appearing at the Red Lion, just down the road. We all decided it would be a good idea to go. We sat at the back of the room as the group went through their paces. The rest of the audience were falling about laughing, whilst the three of us sat at the back of the room with tears running down our cheeks for the whole of the show. I often wonder what the 'Tinkers' thought was going on at the back of the room – I'll ask them one of these days!

Twenty Five

Rome

Shortly after the death of my sister I received a phone call from the landlord of one of my locals, the 'Wheatsheaf'. John Atherton asked if I had anything planned for the forthcoming week. When I answered in the negative he asked if I would like to go to Italy for a week, free of charge! His mother had unfortunately died in Australia and he was off to the antipodes for her funeral. His wife and six others were continuing their planned holiday and I was to make up the eight. I was extremely grateful and had a fabulous week in Rome. The group included a fellow entertainer in Tom Newton, an amazing character, comedian and artist who I'd known all my life. Many years later Tom was to receive the highest accolade possible when he received the M.B.E. for his services to charity. Together with Tom's brother-in-law, the fourth male in our party, was our local Catholic priest whom we'd nicknamed Rick the Vic. Rick had trained for the priesthood in Rome so he knew all the best pubs to go to! He also knew places of interest that most tourists would not know about. I was to have a brilliant week visiting these places of interest and dining out every night in the Eternal City.

The hotel we stayed in was a monastery on the third and fourth floor but the bottom three floors had been made into a hotel to supplement the monks' income. Besides our group of eight, there was a larger party of about 20 students and their tutors from New York City. Tom, being his usual self, introduced himself with the immortal line, "What a coincidence, you lot getting Wigan holidays, same as us!"

We hired a very small mini-bus throughout our stay and Rick was the designated driver as he had an Italian temperament, this meant driving everywhere with one hand constantly pressed on the horn! One day we drove down to the South to see the breathtaking sights of Pompeii. The town had been buried by between four and six metres of ash and pumice following an eruption of the volcano Vesuvius in 79 A.D. That was the end of that until around 1600 when it was accidentally re-discovered. It has been a popular tourist attraction for the last two hundred and fifty years and is one of the most popular Italian destinations. I was amazed at the size of the place, it seemed to go on forever but when I saw Frankie Howerd in his toga, appearing in, 'Up Pompeii' at the coliseum, I was blown away! Only joking!

Following our visit to Pompeii, we called into a shop in the back streets of Naples to buy some wine for our suppers! We bought two huge bottles of home-made firewater that cost a few pence. The journey from Naples to Rome takes a few hours so we were all settling down when we heard a bang, a whimper and a hiss. Following an inspection of the engine by eight people who knew nothing about engines, we decided that the radiator was empty and that it needed topping up with water. Unfortunately, we had no water and we were on a motorway in the middle of the countryside. We were informed by Rick that leaving a vehicle unattended on the motorway was a serious offence in Italy, so we had to stay with the van. Mobile phones were unheard of in those days and we couldn't see any emergency phones by the roadside. We needed to repair the bus, we needed water! Some bright spark said, "Why don't we use the wine we've just bought!"

"But that's sacrilege", I said. "You can't waste all that wine on an engine!"

"But we haven't got any water, what else can we use?"

"Recycled wine!"

"What do you mean?"

"Well we could drink the wine first and fill up the bottles with you know what!"

So we all proceeded to guzzle down the wine and wait a while until recycling could take place!

Eventually both bottles were filled and poured into the radiator. We even had to ask Rick if we could have some 'holy water' from him. Once the radiator was topped up we began slowly to make our way back to Rome, that is until the whole thing blew up and we were obliged to make alternative travel arrangements. Several of the party hitch-hiked back to Italy's capital city and there lies another story. Tom tells of being picked up by a wagon driver who offered himself, his wife Margaret and Angela a lift back to Rome. Whilst driving along the motorway the driver points out that he was captured by the British during the Second World War and was a prisoner for several years. During the journey the driver indicates the hills of Monte Casino that were bombarded by Allied forces during the month of February, 1944.

"You English, boom, boom, boom!" he exclaims and gesticulates to Tom and his two female companions. They are picturing scenes from all the horror movies that they've ever seen, whilst thinking they would never see the rest of us again! Fortunately, he was quite a nice bloke and bought them all a drink at the service station. That's not a very good ending but it's the truth!

Twenty Six

Singing

I began singing more often. I'd always sung from being young but this was more in front of an audience. My brother and I sang regularly at the Youth Club, usually for audiences consisting of pensioners who lived locally and were invited as a sort of 'International relations' exercise. With upwards of two hundred people attending seven nights a week, there was bound to be tensions amongst the surrounding estate. Jimmy had learned how to play guitar so that he could sing his favourite Bob Dylan songs. He was completely self taught but gave a very good impression of someone who knew what they were doing!

We'd sing at the Youth Club, we'd sing at the pub and we regularly sang on the motorway! The M61 was completed around this time and when we didn't fancy going home we'd get someone to drive us to the newly built service station at Anderton. We'd have supper, sing a few songs, then it's over the motorway bridge and back home! Now that was living! One night the staff didn't think it was appropriate for a group of lads to be singing songs so they sent for the police, who duly arrived within ten minutes (they probably fancied a bit of supper too), told us not to be naughty, then continued to order their subsidised meal! Motorways were relatively new to us in those days and we found that it was quite an adventure to have a ride there. They'd welcome us with open arms nowadays because nobody ever calls at that particular Service Station.

One night we were asked to entertain in the function room of the Red Lion pub. This was later to become a folk club and home to the resident group 'The Auld Triangle' for many years. They won the Best Folk Club in the U.K. in 2000, so belated congratulations to them! During the evening I was approached by a bloke who I didn't recognise, though I was later to find out that his son was a friend of mine. He asked if I would be interested in making a bit of money from my singing. He offered to organise auditions around the local Social Clubs; he would make arrangements, provide transport and negotiate finances for a small fee. I thought it wouldn't do any harm to give it a go, but what about my brother Jimmy. "Oh, I'm only talking about you!" he answered.

His name was Arthur Swift and he would phone up Social Clubs and ask if his protégé (me!) could audition at their club. Arthur wasn't an agent or manager, just a keen amateur who thought I had something to offer. We'd go along to a club and do a couple of songs when the paid artiste was having a break. I only had about four pieces of music at the time so there wasn't much chance of doing a full nights' entertainment. We travelled around Bolton, Wigan and Leigh which was far enough, as there were Social clubs on almost every corner.

Around this time, time there was a TV programme called 'Wheeltappers and Shunters Social Club', featuring Colin Crompton and Bernard Manning. It was an extremely popular programme showing very famous acts working in what they portrayed as a caricature of Social Clubs of the time. Colin Crompton portrayed the Club Chairman who had his own microphone and could interrupt anyone performing. Norman Collier always swears that Colin Crompton pinched his act, especially the part when the microphone didn't work properly! Bernard was the club compere who introduced all the acts. Both would insult each other and the acts that were about to perform. Audiences who watched on TV thought it to be a gross exaggeration of what really went on. Not on your life! If anything, they were far better behaved than these people in real life.

Many comics who worked on this show, which was many years before the dawn of 'The Comedians' T.V. show, rehearsed during the day. As the show was being recorded, Bernard Manning reputedly told the gags that his guests had told at rehearsal, leaving the comics completely bewildered as to how they should continue.

Before I go on to tell some of the true instances that I witnessed or was part of I'd like to go back to the name, 'Wheeltappers and Shunters'. Both names seem an exaggeration to begin with but both were actual occupations on the railways. A "shunter" was responsible for sorting out where each train wagon should be. They would make sure that empty wagons were returned to their owners or forwarded for re-loading and that others were sent to their various destinations. A 'Wheeltapper' did exactly as the name implies. They checked that the wheels on the bogeys did not have any cracks in them by tapping them with a long hammer. The resultant sound was either clear, indicating a good wheel, or dull, which meant it needed repairing. They also had to check that the axles boxes were not overheating by touching them with the back of their hands - I think you can work that one out for yourself! If they ended up in hospital with second degree burns it was fairly obvious that the axles needed to be looked at!

So Arthur and I would spend a Saturday evening driving around these clubs in the hope that we could get work. Looking back, it was a frightening apprenticeship but we somehow got through it all. We'd arrive, make ourselves known to the Club Secretary, sort out my music with the organist and drummer, sing a couple of songs and, if they were interested in booking me, it was over to Arthur to talk money; big money in those days, sometimes as much as £6! Every club had an organist and drummer so the fact of the matter was generally, the smaller the club, the 'less able' was their musical prowess. Some were unbelievably bad and some were exceptionally good. The 'backing' (as they were called) could make or break an artiste so it was particularly important that it was checked thoroughly before you went on stage. You needed to tap out the rhythm several times and then they played it at whatever speed they fancied! There were lots of brass bands in the area during this period and some of these organists played every tune in the style of a brass band march; ballads, pop tunes, songs from the shows all got the same treatment. You knew immediately the band started if you had a chance of a booking. Some of the musicians, if you could call them that, would make a complete mess of the backing, if they didn't like the look of you, just so you wouldn't get a booking.

One of my earliest recollections was doing an audition at a club in Halliwell, Bolton. The backing was good and the audience really liked what I did. I confidently came off stage and expected Arthur to get me a good deal. He was waiting for me in the changing room and said, "Great spot Tony, I'll start off at a good price and then talk him down". Shortly afterwards, in walks the Concert Secretary with diary in hand, "Well, listening to the crowd out there I suppose I'll have to give you a booking."

"Thanks a lot!" I say, "they were a great crowd."

"So, how much do you want?" continues the concert secretary.

Arthur, thinking he's on a winner, adjusts his tie, smiles at the guy and says, "I was thinking about nine or ten"

The bloke looks Arthur in the face and says, "Was that shillings or pounds?", closes the diary and walks out of the room, slamming the door behind him.

I often wonder how some of these people who appear on the talent shows of today would have fared in such a situation. They fall apart if Simon Cowell raises an eyebrow. Every Concert Chairman in those days saw themselves as a Simon Cowell; a star maker or breaker and some didn't use Simon Cowell's diplomacy! You had to have quite a strong back to take the criticism of the majority of these little 'Hitlers'. It was rumoured that a job like theirs was financially beneficial, as everything that went in and out of the premises was 'cash'. It was a joke that went around the circuit in those days that the first prize in any raffle was twelve months on the Committee!

Every weekend Arthur and I would travel around our locality to be insulted by Concert Chairmen who occasionally gave us a 'booking'. Today, it's fairly well known that I know hundreds of songs but in those days, not only did you need to know the songs but you needed the sheet music as well. Most of the organists would utterly refuse to play a piece of music without the actual 'dots' as they were known. In some cases this was a bit of a ploy as they couldn't read the music in front of them. I had, by that time expanded my repertoire of sheet music to around twelve pieces, two of which I didn't know but would risk them if things got desperate. So, although I was eager to get myself a paid job in one of these places, I was also conscious of the fact that I hadn't enough material to last a full evening. It meant that I would sing six or seven songs in my first spot and repeat half of them when I returned to stage later in the evening. Only the organist and drummer ever noticed, the audience were never really interested in what I did, or anybody else for that matter. It was said many times during those days that audiences wouldn't give order even if Frank Sinatra was on stage.

Twenty Seven

A Typical Night

After a nervous meal I would quickly wash, shave and get into my only suit with white shirt and as gaudy a tie as possible! Gaudy ties seemed to be the norm in 'showbiz' in those days. I'd sit in the front room and anxiously wait for Arthur to appear. On arrival, I'd jump into the front seat and after a few words of greeting he'd go through his 'pep' talk for the evening.

"Now tonight, we're going to such and such a club. You're doing three songs from about five past nine, just before the Bingo. I've spoken to the Club secretary and he says they like Songs from the Shows and they also like a good dance! For God sake don't do 'Ten Guitars', everybody does that! Do that one by Tony Bennett and tell that joke about the three blokes in the pub. Follow it with that one from South Pacific and finish with a Neil Diamond so they can get up if they want. Keep it slick and pretend you don't come from Westhoughton! I think we should get a booking here 'cos the Secretary seems alright – not like that miserable bugger last week. Anyway relax and enjoy yourself!"

Relax after that lot! I was panicking enough before I had to contend with all that! How do I pretend I'm not from Westhoughton? I really don't want to start talking with an American accent like a lot of them do. They sound ridiculous. Maybe it's OK if I pretend I'm from Wigan? All the audience will be and at least they'll understand what I'm talking about. I stew for another twenty minutes whilst Arthur drives us to the club – well near the club! He usually gets lost and we have to ask the way which means we are usually on the last minute.

One night we got quite lost and needed to stop to ask the way. The only person we could see was a bloke who was certainly 'under the weather'. He looked like he'd been out all day and was sitting in a shop doorway. I jumped out of the car and walked towards him.

"Excuse me mate, you don't know where Bamfurlong Labour Club is, do you?"

The bloke staggers to his feet and thinks for a few minutes. "Bamfurlong Labour Club? I'm sure I should know where that is."

"Don't worry, I'll ask someone else."

"Bamfurlong Labour Club?" The drunk staggers towards Arthur's car and walks round to the driver's side, "Hey pal! Where are you going?"

Arthur innocently replies, "I'm off to Bamfurlong Labour Club."

The drunk rushes round the car and nearly falls over me as he says, "You'll not believe me pal, but I've got you a lift!"

We eventually arrive at our destination and manage to park. Arthur leads the way and explains to the doorman that we are doing an audition.

"Doesn't matter what you're doing, it will still cost you 10p if you're not a member. You'll have to sign in! One of you can sign for both but it's still 10p each! Compere for tonight will be down at the front, he's the one with the wig and sequinned jacket, called Vince Fontaine, his real name's Billy Smith from Platt Bridge!"

We pay the 20 pence, sign the book, receive a tiny piece of paper which is apparently our receipt and membership card for the evening and push open the saloon-style doors to be confronted by Vince Fontaine with 'probably the best backing in Platt Bridge!', Tommy on organ and Fred on drums! The noise is deafening, Vince is trying to overpower Fred and Tommy whilst the audience are in the lead by about ten decibels!

Slowly I edge myself along to the front seats 'Reserved for the Artiste'. It's quite difficult because my feet are sticking to the carpet and I am quite mesmerised by Vince's toupee which is several shades redder than his own hair. Tobacco smoke permeates the whole room and a blue cloud is hovering over most of the 'blue rinsed' heads. There's a smell of meat pies and mushy peas which doesn't particularly mix with stale beer and smouldering cigs! Tommy and Fred have done this song a million times and are having a chat about the winner of the 3.15 at Haydock Park. Tommy manages to light a 'Park Drive' from the dying embers of the one dangling from his bottom lip whilst Fred sticks in an extra two or three 'fills' to show that he's the master, whilst mouthing to the waiter that they need two more pints of mild and one bitter immediately!

Vince reaches the climax of the song and goes into a falsetto scream through the last couple of bars whilst gyrating around the stage like a Tasmanian devil, until his face colouring matches his hairpiece!

Tommy meanwhile, is having his own palpitations because the end of his cig has fallen onto his lap and he is rivalling Fred for speed of hands as he tries to brush away the burning embers that have ignited his piano stool and trouser leg. The song finishes with a drum roll and cymbal crash, organ at full volume and Vince struggling to get his breath back. Nobody in the room claps! It's as though everyone in the room is living in a parallel universe and didn't even see poor Vince. He worked his socks off and got absolutely no recognition from anyone in the room!

Immediately follows a drum roll and fanfare from the organ. Vince bounces to the front of the stage and declares, "What a fabulous crowd we've got here tonight!" ....am I watching the same show or have I been teleported to the same parallel universe?

"We've got a tremendous show for you tonight ladies and gentlemen. Just back from a tour of Turkey............... or was it Torquay, TV and recording star, a favourite on Radio Platt Bridge the amazingly talented........ all the way from Bickershaw, let's hear it for Nancy 'tickles your fancy' Stardust. We've got a lad here, who's starting his career in this wonderful world of Showbiz, we don't know what he's going to be like but, just in case, let's hear it for Tony Bennett! We've got the best duo in clubland behind me....which is a bit worrying....let's hear it for the extraordinary Tommy on organ and the man with the world at his fingertips, Freddy on drums!

Without further ado let's get on with the show.....don't forget, pies are available all night at Florrie's Fabulous Feedery.....raffle tickets only 10p for twenty tickets. To open the box tonight, with a jackpot of thirty five pounds, only seventeen keys left. That's all I think.....off we go with the first flyer of the night.....any one line pays £2.50......EYES DOWN LOOK IN! Your first number.....!"

My ears are tingling.....I think I must have gone deaf.....I can't hear anything apart from Vince shouting out the occasional Bingo number. What was ten seconds ago a crowd from Wembley stadium has now become the audience for a major chess tournament! Boris Spassky and Bobby Fischer are deep in thought as are the two hundred strong audience. Then I realise that it's not Tommy or Fred, or Vince, Tony Bennett or even Nancy 'tickles your fancy' Stardust that all these people are here for. I don't think they're even here for the cheap beer or

161

Florrie's meat pies. No, the definite star of this show is.....BINGO!

This is all a new experience for me and as I'm trying to soak it all up, Fred and Tommy stick their heads out of the dressing room.......dressing room, that's a laugh.....it's just an oversized cupboard containing two chairs and a massive mirror that covers one wall. The other walls are filled with photographs of other artistes who have graced this stage......Gladys Alsopp and her Performing Pigeon......the many voices of the multi-talented Freddy Diamond......the Sultry sounds of the Sexy Sirens of Standish......AND......there in the corner is Nancy 'tickles your fancy' Stardust with her skirt round her ankles, straightening her bra! "Don't worry about me love, you'll soon get used to it! Me love, I've seen it all before......blokes are allus dropping their pants when I'm around!"

With my jaw briefly catching my knees, I try to tell Tommy and Fred how I'd like my music played but all my senses are being bombarded to such a degree that I wish I was in that parallel universe that seems so utterly more preferable to what's happening to me in this place!

Fred interjects, "You're not doing 'Ten Guitars' are you?"

"No" I reply, "Arthur didn't think it would go down well"......Arthur, what happened to Arthur? I stick my head out of the changing cupboard and he's sitting there in a kind of suspended animation, slowly glancing around the room, trying to take it all in......obviously he's as used to all this as I am!

"I think I'll start off with this one please......keep the tempo fairly fast and as I can think of nothing else to say, I continue, I think I'll just leave it all to you." Just then there's a hammering on the door, "Make less noise in there, we're trying to play a game!" I pass the other two copies of music to Fred, thank them both and just go outside to my seat remembering I'm allowed to breathe but not too loudly.

"Maggie's den, number TEN!"

"House!" "House!"

"That's two houses called on number ten. Mervyn, check that one for me please and Nigel, the woman in the corner near the gents!"

Several minutes later "Those houses are correct! £1.25 to that gentleman and the same to Maggie over there! So that's that for the moment. Give me two minutes and it's on with the show!"

Vince's head pops out of the changing room, "Anything you want me to say about you? Where are you from? You'll be straight on after Nancy, three songs? You're not doing 'Ten Guitars' are you?"

I think Arthur answered all those questions. I'm still reeling from seeing Nancy in the altogether!

"Please welcome on stage, the star of TV, Radio and following her visit to New York.......sorry!......near York! Ladies and Gentlemen, tonight's star turn......Nancy 'tickles your fancy' Stardust!"

"Well howdo! How are you all? Long time since I was here. Lovely to see Vince and the lads again. Great club, we'll have a great night! Did you hear about those two blokes in a pub......"

So, she's not a singer, she's a comic! There's almost as much showing as there was in the changing room! I look round the club and all the blokes are glued to Nancy's assets! I don't recognise any of the gags and the audience only laugh when Nancy swears......and she does quite a lot of that! She's loud, brash and filthy, just what they want. How on earth am I going to cope.......will they like me......will I sing the right songs......will Vince's toupee stay on for the night, will Nancy's assets stay in? Is showbiz really the life for me? Should I leave now?

Twenty Eight

Now It's My Turn

The next twenty minutes becomes a blur until Arthur arouses me from my thoughts with, "Do you not think you should go and get ready?" I wander into the cupboard and slowly fasten my tie, glancing as I do so, at the many pictures that decorate the walls. Most of them have been defaced by someone using a marker pen. Gladys Alsopp has a ring through her nose and her pigeon has grown a huge beak, Freddy Diamond now sports a beard and glasses whilst the Sexy Sirens of Standish have had most of their front teeth blacked out. There are advertisements for everything showbiz including recording studios, insurance companies, costumes, hairstylists, photographers, sound equipment and musical instruments.

I'm finding myself quite amused, not necessarily by the photos but by the way they've been doctored, when I realise in three minutes I'll be in front of that baying horde, trying to convince them that I'm starting on a career ladder that is worthwhile. Vince bounds back into the dressing room; obviously Nancy's nearing the end of her 'spot'.

"Good luck, kid! I'll bring you straight on. Don't forget, don't do Ten Guitars!"

"Ladies and gentlemen, the fabulous Nancy 'tickles your fancy' Stardust. You'll be seeing more of her later....although some of you blokes might have a coronary if you saw more of her! Boom, boom! It's on with the show....without further delay please welcome on stage a young lad who's making his debut at this club.....and with the look of him, probably his debut at any club, all the way from Westhoughton, Tony Dennett!" Vince passes me the mike and he's off to the bar!

The duo play an entrance fanfare and I walk on to the sound of clinking glasses, orders for drinks, old Joe having an argument with his missus and one or two 'one armed bandits' clunking away but definitely no applause. I shuffle to the front of the stage on quaking legs that really don't want to go forward. I turn to Tommy and Fred and off they go!

The music's too fast but there's nothing I can do about it! I look out to the crowd and it's obvious that nobody gives a damn about Tony Dennett, Bennett, or whatever I'm called. I'm racking my brains to remember the next line of the song but it's difficult to concentrate. I've spotted old Joe and his missus having a row and just can't take my eyes off them.

I can hear, "I told you I wanted a schooner of sweet sherry not dry and them crisps are salt and vinegar not cheese and onion!"

"Bugger off woman! And next time you want a drink you can go and get it yourself!"

"That's gratitude for you. All I wanted was a drink and some crisps. I cook and clean for you every day and all you do is watch telly!"

"I'm not watching telly when I'm on't' bloody coal face, trying to earn a crust so you can spend it on schooners o' sherry!"

"Oh, shut up and sit down, there's a lad on stage trying his best. Give him a minute. Bingo's on next and there's a £5 jackpot! I'll even buy you a pint if I win. Now sit deawn an shut it!"

My mouth is getting dryer by the second and I'm having trouble breathing.....what song am I singing?.....where am I?

My lips begin to quiver as does my hand holding the microphone. I bring up the other hand to stop the shaking and, using both hands.....my hands shake twice as much! Just at that moment my right leg begins to tremble so I forget about my hands. It doesn't stop them shaking, I've just forgotten about them! So with dry lips and trembling limbs I continue singing a song I've forgotten.....my brain doesn't remember the words.....fortunately my mouth does! How can that happen? Don't worry about it now Tony.....that is your name isn't it?

Suddenly we've reached the end of the first song. What happens next? Do I speak to the audience who, by the way, have begun to get up and walk round the room, talking to friends, buying bingo tickets and ordering drinks. They don't know I've finished......but equally, did they ever notice that I'd started? I turn to Tommy and Fred who are respectively lighting a Park Drive and downing a pint in two gulps!

"Ready, lad? Should we just start? They're not listening anyway. Don't worry, you're no worse than anybody else! Two, three, four......"

The next song goes down just as well as the first. Old Joe and his missus have settled down and are getting quite friendly. Things are looking up and I'm beginning to relax somewhat.....still shaking, still got dry lips but one or two of the crowd are actually looking at me. Does that mean I'm going down well? Who knows......only one more song to go... This is the one that they can dance to. *Give it all you've got, Tony, you may get a booking out of this!*

"Thanks everybody for being such a great audience, hope to see you again. I'd like to finish with this one. If anyone would like to get up and have a dance please be my guest. Thanks to Tommy, Fred and Vince for their help, here goes......"

Tommy and Fred start and I begin singing......oh, I've developed a twitch over my eye which complements the trembling in my hands and wobbling in my legs. Every part of my body has started sweating and it's beginning to run down my face, arms and legs! This is probably how Elvis started, I lie to myself or, perhaps the reason 'Shaking Stevens' got his name. I try to move around the stage in an attempt to show the audience I can dance (which I can't). Two old dears have appeared on the dance floor but are struggling to find what dance they can do to this particular rhythm. After three attempts they give up and go back to their table. I finish the song and I'm sure I hear a clap somewhere in the room! I dash off stage as Vince appears in the wings. He wrestles the microphone from my hand and bounces to the centre of the stage.

"What did you think about that ladies and gentlemen? Let's go straight into the next game, £2 any line and £3 for a full house with a jackpot of £20 if claimed in 30 numbers or less". No mention of me......it was as if I'd not been there!

So that was it! I sit down as Arthur walks in. "Well, what do you think?" he asks cheerfully.

"Just give me a minute to finish this pint and we'll talk about it."

"You went down really well! A bloke near me said that you were the best act they've had here in ages!"

"But nobody was listening and hardly anybody clapped!"

"Oh, they're like that round here but they still enjoyed it!"

"Does that mean I might get a booking?"

"Well, there's something I forgot to tell you about that."

"What do you mean? Have you not spoken to Vince?"

"Oh, Vince, he's only the compere. The Concert Secretary does all the bookings and he won't give anybody an engagement unless he's seen them himself."

I'm getting rather exasperated, "So what did he think of my spot?"

"Well, that's the trouble", says Arthur, "He's on his holidays in Benidorm this week, so we'll have to come back next week so that he can see you for himself.....but I'm sure he'll like what he sees."

On his holidays in Benidorm.....come back next week.......likes what he sees?

"So all that was for nothing!"

"Well I wouldn't say that. It's really good experience for you and they really enjoyed it......and

Tommy and Fred are very good......and Vince was great......not forgettin' that you had the chance to work with Nancy.

So I collect my music from Tommy and start making my way to the back of the hall. My feet still stick to the carpet and the smell is still repugnant but I think I might try one of Florrie's pies to eat on the way home. As we approach the entrance I hear his dulcet tones as he starts singing....... "I have a band of men and all they do is play for me......"

He's singing "Ten Guitars", the bugger! Well that's showbiz and now I've joined the club and I love it! All setbacks forgotten, I've been bitten by the bug!

"Well that's the end of that! Great night! Where are we going next week?"

Thus began a weekly outing to the 'clubland' around Lancashire. This time during the late 60's and all through the 70's was the zenith of that type of entertainment. There were clubs everywhere and catering for everything; Labour clubs, Liberal clubs, Conservative clubs, Working Mens clubs, Irish clubs, Polish clubs, Ukrainian clubs, Caribbean clubs, not forgetting the Pigeon Fanciers club, the Botanical Gardens club (commonly known as the 'Cabbage' clubs), the Miners clubs, Football, Cricket, Rugby, Bowls, the list goes on and on.....

All these establishments catered for people with similar attitudes, be it towards work, politics, sport or background. There was one overriding principle that all these institutions provided, conviviality, entertainment and cheap beer! Very cheap beer in the more popular spots! In one club the barman even offered free beer to anyone who could order a cocktail that he didn't know how to make. For weeks people came from far and wide to beat him at his game, ordering the most obscure cocktails they could think of but the barman knew them all. That was until one day a man ordered a "Southampton". The barman is stumped and has to admit that it's one he's never heard of.

"I'll get you a pint once you've told me how to make one", insists the barman, "so what do I do?"

The bloke smiles and says, "All you need is a large port!"

Twenty Nine

Social Services

After a couple of years working in the school for the deaf, I apply for a job with Bolton Social services. Bolton is divided into six areas and the organisation had decided to employ a young trainee in each area whom they would train up and be fast tracked to management positions. I was, amazingly, offered a position in my home patch of Westhoughton and Horwich. Westhoughton had just become part of the new administrative county of Greater Manchester and an area within the boundary of the Metropolitan Borough of Bolton following Local Government Reorganisation on April 1st 1974.

As a Lancastrian I find this very difficult to accept and on further inspection I find that I'm not alone! However, everywhere I look it appears that I've nothing to worry about!

"The new county boundaries are solely for the purpose of defining areas of local government. They are

administrative areas, and will not alter the traditional boundaries of Counties, nor is it intended that the loyalties of people living in them will change."
Spokesman for the Department of the Environment 1974.

In 1066 when the Norman hordes invaded our shores Lancashire, as we know it, didn't exist but around 1072, King William gave the land between the rivers Ribble and Mersey respectively together with the area called Amounderness to Roger of Poitou. Amounderness was possibly named after a Norse warlord or a Viking who settled in the area. Twenty years later William Rufus added Lonsdale, Furness and Cartmel to the list, which meant that Roger of Poitou now owned the lands from the Mersey to the River Duddon in the North. The most centrally positioned town was Lancaster so Roger built a castle there and the lands became known as 'the honour of Roger of Poitou' or 'the honour of Lancaster'.

Shortly after the start of the 12th Century, Roger supported his brother in an unsuccessful rebellion against King Henry I so all his lands were taken from him and given to the grandson of William the Conqueror. In 1168 the lands were eventually given the title of 'the county of Lancashire' under King Henry II. Strategically, Lancashire was given more responsibility because of its location. It was very important as it lay between England and the marauding Celtic and Rangers fans from across the border to the North.

So for over 800 years Lancashire has been one of Britain's greatest counties. By the 1830's approximately

85% of all manufactured cotton in the world was processed in Lancashire. Lancashire was a major mover and shaker in the Industrial Revolution where innovations, which affect the world as we know it today, took place almost on a daily basis. In the Census of 1971, Lancashire had the largest population of all the counties in Britain.

So a bloke in an office in London decides to get rid of it all. "We'll make Manchester and Liverpool into counties and we'll move a bit of Lancashire into Cheshire and some into Westmorland but we'll call that place Cumbria!" But the most mortal of all sins was when he said, "Oh and we can move that bit of Lancashire into Yorkshire and give Lancashire a few Tykes!" And the same bloke expected us all to say *That's fine! No problem!*

So the 'Friends of Real Lancashire' was born who's only aim is to re-instate in peoples minds that the old County boundaries were fine as they were and that we should celebrate the fact that Warrington and Bolton and Coniston and Westhoughton are all part of the great county of Lancashire. I'm sure that if you're a Yorkshireman reading this you'd feel exactly the same way if it was done to your fabulous county.

I think that last sentence should give me a few 'brownie' points when it comes to a modern day 'War of the Roses'!

That's another thing, the Wars of the Roses! We see it as an ongoing rivalry between the inhabitants of the counties that straddle the Pennines. In actual fact the Wars of the Roses had very little to do with our two great counties and hardly anything to do with the great cities of Lancaster and York!

John of Gaunt was the first Duke of Lancaster and, following his marriage to Blanche and the death of his father-in-law, he held at least thirty castles and estates across England and France and was the greatest landowner in the North of England. His brother Edmund, was given the title, Duke of York and thus began a struggle that was to last for thirty years. Both parties wanted power and the greatest power in England was in the hands of the monarch. They couldn't negotiate who had what, so they decided to fight for what they wanted. Hostilities opened with a Yorkist victory at St. Albans where Henry VI was taken prisoner and eventually ended with the defeat of Richard III at Bosworth, near Leicester (nowhere near Lancashire!) All told, there were three kings from the house of Lancaster and three kings from the House of York so you could say it was a draw! Finally, King Henry VII, who was also known as Henry Tudor combined the two famous roses into what was to become the Tudor Rose (A white and red rose combined).

Although the rose was occasionally used as a symbol for these great houses, the participants wore the badges of their lords when taking up their cudgels. Henry's troops at the Battle of Bosworth followed the 'red dragon' whilst Richard III legions stood behind the 'white boar'. Our present Queen is the Duke of Lancaster and her son, Andrew is the Duke of York, so if they had a row would it reverberate around Barnoldswick and Barrow? I think not!

All this is a very simplified version of these events and even though the Wars had very little to do with the counties of Yorkshire and Lancashire try telling that to the fans of Leeds United when they play Manchester United at Old Trafford or Elland Road or equally fans of Wigan and Bradford when the 'Warriors' lock horns with the 'Bulls' at Rugby League.

So I begin working in Westhoughton and Horwich as a 'generic' Social worker. Prior to re-organisation there were welfare officers for the elderly, welfare workers for the young and welfare workers for the disabled. A generic social worker would deal with all manner of problems, in other words a 'jack of all trades'. So I worked with men and woman who had been specialists in a certain field but Social Services, in their wisdom, made them all leave their zones of comfort to deal with problems amongst society that they weren't 'au fait' with. They say that things always go round in a circle and nowadays social workers specialise in an area of social work that is best suited to their qualifications and qualities.

A few things spring to mind when I think of my days with Social Services. Like the forty year old Downes Syndrome woman that nobody knew about until her elderly parents became ill and incapable of looking after her, or, the ninety year old woman who I visited because someone had reported that she might need help. On the first visit, it was noticeable that the lady had broken her arm in the past as it had two angles in it; one at the elbow and another between the elbow and her wrist. She'd obviously broken it and done nothing about it so it healed this way – she must have spent many weeks in agony! And finally, the house in Horwich, that still had gas lighting in the mid-seventies! The house was rented for a tiny amount and the tennant refused to allow alterations and modernisation because it would mean a hike in the weekly rent!

On one occasion I was asked to accompany a Senior Social Worker to the house of a possibly violent man. My senior instructed me to try and keep calm. "Whatever you do Tony, don't stand over him. Your height might cause him to attack!"

Keeping this in mind, we attend the house and were both asked to take a seat. We did so and were offered a cup of tea, which we accepted. The interview was going reasonably well but it was obvious that the bloke could 'flip his lid' at any time. Eventually he was asked to sign a particular form which I'd unfortunately left in the car. I was asked to go and get the relevant paperwork but all the time I'm thinking, *"Don't stand up, don't overwhelm him, keep calm!"*

So I stand, but not to my full height and proceed towards the door feeling a bit like John Cleese doing his 'Ministry of Silly Walks' impression! I was only short of a false moustache, thick glasses and a cigar to stop me looking like Groucho Marx!

Thirty

Weekends on the Road

Following my first night out with Vince and the gang, Arthur and I began touring the locality every weekend, attempting to get myself a paid 'gig'. Now, I've often wondered where the term 'gig' came from and after trying to find out, I'm not sure whether I should have bothered. A gig is a term used in fishing for a spear like implement for catching fish; it's also the term for a small boat that can be attached to a larger boat for easier access in areas the bigger boat can't manoeuvre; it's a small blade that wrestlers might use to inflict cuts to their own body; a miner's cage is sometimes called a gig; it's a light wheeled carriage driven by a horse. Now that last one might be nearing the answer to my quest. It is said that black musicians in New Orleans were not allowed to busk on the streets. So they overcame that law by playing music aboard a 'gig', whilst travelling around town. Now whether this is right or not I don't know but it is a good enough reason to include it here!

There's another definition that might be of interest. In the Merriam-Webster dictionary I found that gig could be a person of odd or grotesque appearance. And, finally, I found a place in Washington State, USA, called Gig Harbour (although they spell it Harbor!) that holds an annual maritime festival called the 'Gig Festival'. SO, it's possible to go to Gig on a gig to do a gig with a gig! And while you're there you could go into the harbour on a gig with a gig but watch out you don't cut yourself on a gig!.....bum....bum....

We'd carry on touring the locality for work but it was extremely time consuming and not very practical or profitable. There were two other ways to bypass these auditions for solo gigs. We could enter talent contests, which could be far more profitable if you won, or we could try out a 'Shop Window' audition. These shows were very difficult to access when I was starting in my musical career because everyone wanted to do them. Basically, a club would organise a 'shop window' show and invite all the concert secretaries from their locality and sometimes much farther afield. This meant that, instead of trying to entertain a club full of people and one concert secretary, you entertained a room full of concert secretaries. Now if you think my first audition was nerve wracking, just imagine a room full of Simon Cowells, all out for blood! You'd be expected to do a twenty minute 'spot' and then sit in the audience until the show had finished. There would be approximately a dozen artists trying to get work. At the end of the show, you, or your advisor, namely Arthur, would be approached by the head of the Concert Secretaries (Mr. Big!) and be asked for your fee. He would then try to knock that fee down because, instead of giving you one gig, he would be negotiating for all the clubs that liked what they had seen. He'd expect to halve what was originally asked for but in Arthur's case, half of nothing is still nothing! No, that's a bit unfair but still, half of ten is not very much when two of you are sharing it!

This got us several bookings in areas that we'd not explored and work that we weren't quite sure how to deal with! For example, I got a booking via a 'shop window' for two nights work at Leigh Casino. I'm in the big time now, I thought! My fee for two nights work was a princely £12. For that I was expected to perform for forty minutes each night starting at about 8.30p.m. Friday would be my first night and for the whole of the preceding week I 'walk' through the show in my head. I'll start off with this song, straight into the next which will be such and such. That's when I'll start talking; I'll tell them where I'm from and finish with that particular gag. Then I'll walk around the stage as I'm introducing the next song; I think that's where I'll do the ballad I've just learned. Then I'd correct myself, start all over again and change the whole routine. *It's so important! You've a chance for a big break here if the show goes well! Could lead to lots more bookings. The bloke who owns the Casino is an agent and might sign me up! What should I wear?*

And so it goes on! I can't stop thinking about the show all week. Eventually Friday arrives and Arthur picks me up early so that we can sort everything out. He gives me my 'pep' talk and explains the possible importance of the gig. We arrive and go to the stage door;

first time I've ever been through a stage door! I'm shown the way to my dressing room and the backing 'band' are pointed out to me. I'm calling it a band because it's more than just an organist and drummer. This band includes a bass player; how do you get a bass player to turn the volume down.....put some music in front of him!.....What's the difference between a trampoline and a bass.....you take your shoes off to jump on a trampoline!

So I go into their dressing room and sort out the 'dots'. I've only got the sheet music for the organist so they'll have to follow him. I just hope they do! Back to my dressing room and I'm joined by an attractive young lady. She says that she's sharing the dressing room with me because she'll be on later and can change whilst I'm on stage. So to make conversation I say, "Hiya, I'm Tony from Westhoughton. Are you on tonight?"

"Yes, love!"

"Are you singing?"

"No, love!"

"So you're a dancer then?"

"Well sort of, love! Have you not been doing this for long?"

"No, it's my first big booking"

"Well good luck love, I'll probably see you later!"

So she's not a singer and 'sort of' a dancer. I must watch her act, it could be very interesting! Maybe she's a comedy magician?

So it's time for me to get on stage. I'm introduced and slowly walk out to what I expect to be a very quiet, small audience. Well it is only half past eight and the crowds don't usually turn out 'til much later. I emerge through the curtains to be met with a throng of baying young male studs! This isn't at all what I expected but here goes......straight into my first song.......and into the next one......they seem OK! I'll talk to them after this song, maybe even tell a joke if I'm not too nervous.

"Well thanks everyone for that tremendous reception! My name's Tony Berry, I'm from Westhoughton and I'm going to entertain you for the next forty minutes!"

"Bugger off back to Westhoughton!" comes the reply.

"I hope you'll like my rendition of ...."

"We'd like it even better if you'd get off and let us have some real entertainment!"

So I go into the next song. The crowd are buzzing but there seems to be something wrong, some undercurrent! My singing is alright and the band is quite good. It's a good start to their night's entertainment, if I say so myself!

After the next song I don't think I'll say anything. They're getting quite restless and some of them must play rugby league by the looks of 'em. Don't want to upset the natives do I. It's an important booking and the owner might be watching!

So, very slowly my forty minutes is coming to an end. *Well, at least that's it until tomorrow, I just feel sorry for that poor girl who's going to follow me. I hope her magic tricks go well and her 'sort of' dancing will entertain.* I end my final song to chants of "GET 'EM OFF!" and slowly walk towards the changing room when, through the corner of my eye, I spot my changing room companion approaching me. She's covered from head to foot in feathers and already they're beginning to fall to the floor! That's when the penny dropped......I'm just a warm up act for Friday night with the Lads!

I slink off to my changing room, climbing over all sorts of unusual costumes on my way; most of which would make a bishop squirm! How did I not work out what she did for a living! Anyway, she was a really nice girl, I wonder if Arthur would like to stay for an hour or two? I could leave my clothes in here so that I'll have to come back for them later!

Thirty One

Talent Contests

To compete with the Social Clubs during the 60's and 70's pubs organised Talent Shows to attract the public. It worked very much like the shop window auditions mentioned earlier. Acts would 'strut their stuff' for an allotted period of time and once they'd all finished the judges would confer to decide who would come back for the final. The prize money was quite good for the early rounds but when it got to the final there was really big money to be had. As I mentioned earlier, my first annual salary was less than £500. In some of the more prestigious competitions you could compete for at least half of that!

We'd spend a few minutes every day looking through the newspapers to see if there was a talent show in our area. The bigger ones would be mentioned in the paper to attract the better acts, others would be just advertised outside the pub that was to hold the event. We thought it would be sensible to start at the bottom in the hope that we could work our way up to the better quality shows. So began an interlude of competition amongst singers, something I never envisaged doing when I started. However, I was to meet a lot of the same faces during the next few months, we were all chasing after the same dream. We'd sit and listen to each other then try to help with some constructive criticism. Sometimes we'd win a few pounds whilst there were occasions when we'd go home empty handed. On arrival at a venue, we'd say our hellos then go on to discuss our chances. There would always be a few locals who had entered for a laugh and didn't really expect to win anything but generally they were the same faces.

Our greatest rivalry in all these competitions would always be.....kids!....especially pretty young girls of about 7 years of age who would smile through the gap in their milk teeth and sing like Lena Zavaroni! However good or bad they were, if there was a kid in the competition, you knew they would always win, *so you might as well go home now and save your energy!* You never did go home, just in case, but they always won nevertheless! When they'd finished their act there would be roars of approval from mummy, daddy, both pairs of grandparents and as many neighbours as they could muster for the night. It always influenced the judges, if they needed any persuasion. So the regular singers would say their goodbyes to everyone until next time, with a wish that nobody under the age of twelve would be there in future!

I won a couple of Talent shows during this period which got me a few quid and sometimes the odd booking. On one particular final which took place at the Casino

Club in Bolton, one of the judges was the legendary Bernard Manning. Although I didn't win He said that I could have a booking at his famous 'Embassy Club' anytime, "The only thing that boy's lacking is talent and ambition!" he commented. Bernard was a much maligned character who had a reputation for being vulgar and racist. Most people don't realise that he was of Russian, Jewish and Irish descent and raised millions of pounds for charity during his lifetime. His next door neighbour, an Indian doctor, described Bernard as the "perfect gentleman". Not in any way condoning his material, comedians in that era did gags that today would seem distasteful and Bernard was only one in a whole generation of similar stand-up's; his biggest problem was that he was probably the most famous.

I once got to the regional final of a particular Talent Contest that was a nationwide affair. I think it was run by 'No 6', the cigarette company. There were several heats in pubs and clubs but the North West final was to be held at the Cavendish Club in Blackburn. It started quite early for something like this, about 7.00 or 7.30 p.m. This was so that the regular cabaret for that week could go ahead as planned. We were obliged to arrive at approximately 2.00 p.m. so that we could sort out our 'dots' with the backing band. Arthur and I duly arrived and were met with some really obnoxious musicians who were complaining that they had to do more work tonight because of our contest. They continually attempted to put us down and make all the contestants totally inferior to them. I considered 'sticking one' on the organist but thought it might detract from my chances in the show.

I eventually worked my way through the music and slunk back to the changing room in a deep depression. This was not supposed to be like this. I thought musicians stuck up for each other and gave unconditional support. That obviously was not the way here so I hung around 'til it was almost time for the show. The compere for the evening was kind and helpful and my spirits were beginning to lift. Then, all of a sudden, there's a knock on my changing room door and who should pop his face round but Gerry Marsden from Gerry and the Pacemakers. He was Top of the bill on tonight's cabaret and even though I wanted to concentrate on my performance, I was really looking forward to watching his show.

"Alright la! Just thought I'd call and say good luck in the competition. Relax and don't worry, they'll be a good audience tonight. Can I buy you a drink?"

"Thanks, so much, I'd like a pint of bitter please!"

"Billy, go and get this lad a pint of bitter, I'll go and see these other competitors. Good luck again son!"

And he'd gone! But how kind of the guy to do what he did. There was no reason whatsoever for him to become involved but I appreciated it so much and it was never to be forgotten!

It brings to mind the adage, 'Be nice to the people on the way up because you'll meet the same people on the way down!'

Thirty Two

Odds and Sodds

Not only did I do the solo gigs but during this time friends would often ask if I could perform on the same bill as them. We'd get an organist, usually George Twist or John Davies who were both enormously talented keyboard players, my brother-in-law, Kevin, had a set of drums which he brought along! Together with myself, my brother Jim, Johnny Lee and Tom Newton we formed a travelling theatre company. We travelled the length and breadth of Westhoughton with occasional forays towards Bolton or Wigan. It was suggested that we wore something resembling an outfit, rather than a uniform, that would distinguish us as an entity. We all wore black trousers and all agreed that the one thing we had in common was a light blue shirt, so that was arranged. What we didn't realise was that shirts come in a variety of blues! There's pale blue, ultramarine, cobalt blue, Prussian blue, lapis lazuli, sapphire, tiffany blue, electric blue and cyan to name but a few. There's a blue moon, Blue Peter, Blue Ridge mountains in Virginia, Blue Grass music and the Blue Oyster cult; the only thing that was never blue was our material! So on that first night we became 'The Shades of Blue'.

Over the years almost every entertainer in Westhoughton has played with this band so if anyone asked who would be turning up to a particular event we'd always say the same thing. "There'll be a load of Odds and Sods but don't worry you'll have a good time whoever appears". So our name was changed and will forever live in the annals of Westhoughton folklore! The evenings were absolute chaos from beginning to end but all-in-all, everyone had a tremendous night's entertainment. I remember one night when Johnny Lee did his famous 'paper bag' routine. There's an old saying, "He couldn't fight his way out of a paper bag". Well John had a human sized paper bag and he proved the old adage to be true! It was hilarious watching him, writhing on the floor in a desperate but vain attempt to escape!

Thirty Three

Nights Out

When I wasn't off singing we might try a night out in Bolton at the high spots like the Navada (no, that's how it was spelled!), Palais de Danse or Beachcomber. The Navada was a roller skating rink during the week and became a night club at the weekend. As you can imagine, being a roller skating rink, the hall was massive but it always appeared full when we went. Lots of top groups of the day appeared there and we always had a great time. I was there the night that Johnny Kidd and the Pirates were due to entertain us with their eye patches and pirate costumes. Unfortunately he was killed in a car smash just outside Bury. I think Brian Poole and the Tremeloes took their place at the last minute. They were a massive draw in those days and appeared at the Navada regularly. When they started in the music industry they were offered an audition by the Decca recording company in the hope of securing a record deal. They were joined at the same audition by an up and coming group from Liverpool called, yes you've guessed, the

Beatles! Decca had only one contract available and they decided to offer it to Brian Poole and the Tremeloes, arguably making the biggest mistake in musical history! The Tremeloes did quite well, having a string of hits but.....?

The Palais was another large ballroom near the town centre and boasted a 'sprung' floor which, if you stood in the middle, you were moving up and down about two feet. It wasn't the place to be if you'd had one too many drinks. Unlike the Navada, it appeared that most of the girls came here to dance and the boys went to 'pick up' a girl. So you can imagine the scene, all the girls dancing round their handbags, moving up and down in the centre of the room, whilst all the boys walked round the arena choosing who they were going to approach later. By the time it came to make a move they'd lost their courage and the girls were left in their 'Bouncy Castle'. The Palais tended to cater for the older youngsters, if you know what I mean. There was a six or seven piece dance band who played........yes you've guessed it again!.....for dancing! They'd do the crooner sort of material, Sinatra, Dean Martin, etc. When they finished, the stage revolved to reveal the 'star' turn. Great stuff!

The Beachcomber was much smaller than the other two but had a certain charisma that drew you to it. There were lots of small rooms on several floors and it appealed generally to the Bolton 'mods'. Not that I was one but I did enjoy the place. There was a time when a friend of mine was invited there for a night out by the owner. He'd told him to come to the door and ask for him. On arrival, he was refused entry by the 'bouncer' because he was wearing a leather jacket. The jacket was an extremely expensive, tailored coat that had cost my friend a small fortune.

"Don't worry, pal, I've been invited by the owner!" came his reply. When the owner arrived he agreed with the bouncer and said he couldn't come in because of his attire.

"But it's your club and you have invited me!" cried my friend in despair.

"Sorry pal but rules are rules!"

I never forget my sister Anne telling me about a night out that she had in the 60's. She went to the Ritz in Wigan to see, on the same bill, The Rolling Stones, Jimi Hendrix and Englebert Humperdink. What a night! It was even worth enduring Englebert, just to see the other two.....just joking Eng, considering the guy has sold over 150 million albums worldwide including 64 gold and 24 platinum albums. He was born Albert Dorsey, in India, the son of a serving soldier but when he started singing he was known as Gerry Dorsey because he did a great impersonation of Jerry Lewis and that was the name his friends called him! He'd been working under that name for years until he took the name of the 19th century German opera composer of such classics as 'Hansel and Gretel' and the rest, as they say, is history!

Generally though, I'd be more than happy to stay in Westhoughton and have a few pints and a game of darts with my mates. Quite a boring sort of a bloke don't you think? At the end of the night, I'd be walking home, unlike the bloke who staggers out of the pub and walks towards his car. Looking through the bushes is the policeman who been staking out the place for the last couple of nights. The bloke takes five minutes to find the right key, eventually opens the door and falls into the front seat. He's about to start the car when the copper emerges from the bushes brandishing his warrant card.

"Right, got you! Come over to my vehicle please, I'd like you to take a breathalyser test!"

So they both stagger towards the police car and the bloke is bundled into the rear seat. After taking the breath test the policeman is amazed to find that the alcohol reading is zero!

"This can't be right!" retorts the officer.

"Oh, yes it can!" says the bloke, "tonight it's my turn to be the decoy!"

"It only takes one drink to get me loaded, trouble is, I can't remember if it's the thirteenth or fourteenth."
George Burns

Thirty Four

Folk Club

If I had a free Friday I would sometimes go down to the Red Lion pub. They'd just started a folk club there and my brother, Jim, was part of the resident group. The only folk act I'd ever seen before was the Clancy Brothers and Tommy Makem, in Manchester. I'd enjoyed them, so I thought I'd give it a try. I knew quite a lot of the people who came to watch as they were mainly locals. It was in a room upstairs in the pub; there was a small bar at the back of the room which only held about eighty or ninety (that's the room not the bar!) The atmosphere was very relaxed and I was amazed to find that the audience listened to the artist! This was unknown to me as I was used to performing in front of audiences who weren't expected to listen. I would have a microphone turned up to full throttle to overpower anything they could throw at me. Here, in this little room, some of the guests would even sing without a microphone at all! The folk club was organised by a brother and sister, who are still in the business of entertaining. Pat and Michael had their audiences well trained. Should a new member join, who was a regular at the local labour club, she would keep an eye on them. If they so much as blew their noses when someone was singing she would be on them like a ton of bricks. Over the years Pat and Michael have had many partners on stage but they have been the constant in a group known as the Auld Triangle.

It is said that there have been two 'folk revivals' over the years but I would argue that we are in the middle of one at the moment. It started in the 1990's and is still alive today. The main protagonists of this particular resurgence have been the children of the last one! The first and second revivals took place between completely different types of people and equally differing types of musical backgrounds.

The first 'folk revival' took place in the last decade of the nineteenth century into the 1920's. There was a strong desire during the period before the First World War, to make English music 'English'. Old folk tunes were revitalised by the likes of Ralph Vaughan Williams, Gustav Holtz and Frederick Delius to make a distinctive English Classical music. The music was 'rural' in origin and people like Cecil Sharpe, who founded the English Folk Dance Society, wrote about the romantic view of an agricultural society. I can see Mr. Sharpe dancing round the haystacks with his betrothed, listening to 'On Hearing the First Cuckoo in Spring' by Delius, whilst farmer Joe, sitting on his five barred gate, fiddle under chin, recalls how Daisy provided him with four quarts of milk, at the break of dayo!

The second revival, however, which took place after the Second World War, up to the early 70's, reaching its peak during the 50's and 60's, coincided with a similar revival in America. Across the Atlantic, the likes of Pete Seeger, Burl Ives and Woody Guthrie started a movement that was to be continued by artists who became major recording stars like Peter, Paul and Mary, Joan Baez, Bob Dylan and John Denver. Most of these artists were thought to be Communists by the Government and had to suffer to get their music to the people. In England, like America, the revival was led by left wing Socialists and Trade Unionists and in contrast to the rural element of the earlier revival, it used industrial songs and sea shanties. Our revival was led almost entirely by a bloke from Salford called James Henry Miller. His family had moved to Salford from Scotland before he was born. His father had been black-listed in every foundry in Scotland because of his left wing views and moved to Salford to find employment. James, or Jimmie, grew up during the Depression and began writing plays and songs. He changed his name to Ewan MacColl in the 40's, inspired by the 'Lallans' poets of the 19th Century who attempted to create a standard Scots language to preserve their identity in the face of English dominance. MacColl wrote lots of songs that are folk standards nowadays but if you don't like the folk music of England in its' present form then blame Jimmie Miller!

So, Friday night became 'folk night' at the Red Lion. I enjoyed it because amazingly, the audience listened to the artist, who didn't talk with a pseudo-American accent but sang songs that told a story, jokes that were funny and most of them had a drink with them on stage! The only similarity that these places had with the clubs where I sang was the fact that they had auditions! These were actually called 'floor spots' but the overall function was the same; listen to somebody and if they were good, give them a booking! One difference being that some people got up, just to sing a song and not necessarily expect a 'gig' at the end of it! I occasionally sang a song with my brother Jim, for that reason. I didn't want a booking – there was no money in folk singing!

Thirty Five

Home Life

By this time, my brother Jim was married, so I shared a house with the 'queen mother'. My mother and I got on very well together. She would do the housework and cook the meals whilst I paid all the bills and stayed in bed as long as I wanted to! She actually became a friend to my friends and was great when they stopped over (which was most weekends!), even to the point of joining us at Borwick Hall when there was a production on. She wasn't a big drinker but there was the odd occasion when I saw her keeping up with some of the real boozers! One instance springs to mind; she'd had rather more than she should have, so when it was bedtime she had to be carried upstairs! The following morning she was up before the sun and tidied everything up before anyone rose from their slumbers; the previous evening was never to be mentioned, ever again!

The 70's continued outside of Westhoughton, although we'd hear references in our everyday life. On meeting someone we would be greeted by "May the force be with you!" and on leaving a friend at night, the parting shot was usually, "Goodnight John Boy!" There were 'lava lamps' in everybody's bedroom and 'Rubik's cubes' in everyone's pocket! There was a film that became a blockbuster featuring a great white shark and a bloke from Westhoughton! Robert Shaw, who played the part of the shark-hunter, Quint, in the film 'Jaws', was the son of a local doctor, Thomas Shaw, in Bolton Road. At the age of seven he moved, with his family, to the Orkney Islands. He starred in many feature films including, 'The Sting', 'Man for all Seasons' and 'From Russia with Love' but I'll always remember him as Dan Tempest in the television series 'The Buccaneers'. I was looking through his roles and happened to find the name of his ship in the Buccaneers, it was the 'Sultana'. I think they could have chosen something better than a dried up grape, don't you?

" A life on the ocean waves will be, the only life for you and me, we'll live and fight the enemy together!" Ooh, aargh, my hearties!

The seventies also saw the 'Watergate' scandal, which led to the resignation of Richard Nixon. Although he will only be remembered for this scandal, he was responsible for the ending of the Vietnam War. During the early 70's there were many demonstrations against the war and on 4th May 1970, at Kent State University, the demonstrators were shot at by the Ohio State guard. Four people were killed, one of whom, Sandra Lee Scheuer, wasn't even taking part in the demonstration but walking from one class to another. Harvey Andrews wrote a song about the day and I remember a line or two.......

"Hey Sandy, Hey Sandy, why were you the one,
All the years of growing up are wasted now and gone,
Did you see them turn,
did you feel the burn
of the bullets as they flew,
Hey Sandy, hey Sandy just what did you do....."

The major thing to hit this country during the mid-seventies, 1975 to be precise, was that the Conservative party recruited a new leader! Margaret Thatcher was born Margaret Hilda Roberts, the daughter of shopkeeper, Alf Roberts, owner of the corner shop in Coronation Street, Weatherfield, Manchester, until he sold it to Reg Holdsworth. Many other books I have read contradicted this and said that she was from 'down south'! Whichever one you decide to accept, it is well known that she was responsible for a great deal of change in this country. She produced a pair of twins which apparently caused her husband Denis to proclaim, as he turned his back on a Test Match,"My god they look like rabbits, put them back!" Denis Thatcher's family made its fortune in New Zealand, producing weed killer for railway tracks and on return to England founded the Atlas Preservative Company which produced a paint used on ships. He never gave interviews stating, "Whales don't get killed until they spout!"

His son, Mark, has led a colourful life to say the least. Given a four years suspended jail sentence for an attempted coup of Equatorial Guinea, he was allegedly involved in loan sharking and gun running from his base in South Africa and famously got lost in the Sahara desert during the Paris to Dakar rally. Carol, his twin sister, once appeared on a T.V. show called '100% English' in which she took DNA tests to prove her lineage. These tests indicated that she could be descended from a Bedouin Tribe or even a desert farmer from ancient Mesopotamia! Maybe Mark was looking for their relatives when he got lost?

Thirty Six

Haydock

One particular weekend I was booked to appear at Haydock Labour Club. Haydock, near St. Helens, had two labour clubs so they were known as number One and Number Two clubs. Opposite this particular one, (not sure if it was One or Two?) stood the Conservative Club. I arrive as usual, with Arthur, in plenty of time to prepare for the evening. On arrival, I'm astonished to find that the club is packed to the rafters; they usually drift in slowly as the evening progresses but on this particular evening there were well over two hundred people crammed in. This however, is Bingo night and they've all turned out early in the hope of a financial bonanza. I go into the changing closet to prepare for the night, sort out my music with the resident band, speak to the concert chairman and liase with the compere. Once all that lot is sorted I go outside to my reserved seat to join Arthur for a drink.

"This should be a good gig tonight, Arthur!"

"Definitely, they look like a good crowd!"

"Well there's plenty of them, let's just hope so!"

It's approaching my performance time so I go into the changing locker, have a laugh at the defaced photographs on the wall, straighten my tie, give me shoes a polish on the back of my trousers and off we go!

I'm introduced to the audience by the compere and so I nod to the organist to start playing and I walk onto stage to be greeted by......an empty room! Maybe a dozen, certainly no more than that, are watching my act. *What on earth is going on*? I say to myself as I nervously go through the routine without too much enthusiasm. *They've never seen me before here so it can't be me, can it? Unless some of them saw me last week in Ashton and word's got around!*

I suddenly realised that I must be improving in confidence because I'm thinking of something else other than the next line in the song. Every connotation goes through my mind as to why they've all disappeared. I slowly work my way through the spot, one more song to go, then I'll find out....."Tell me when will you be mine....tell me Quando, Quando, Quando......."

Immediately I walk off stage, I quickly change into my jeans and tee shirt and think I'll make my way to the seat next to Arthur, he'll surely know what the problem is! I open the door......and the room is completely full again with over 200 people jostling round the tables and ordering drinks!

"What's going on, Arthur?"

"I'm buggered if I know! When you went into the changing room before, they all stood up and walked out and then when you came off stage they all came back in!"

"Do you think they saw me at Ashton last week and told all their mates?"

"I doubt it, there were only about twenty in that club last week. Unless they've got plenty of mates! Maybe the Concert Chairman will be able to help, I'll go and ask him"

Arthur walks slowly to the back of the room and becomes embroiled in a long conversation with the bloke. They seem to be laughing and he's pointing to the entrance. Several nerve racking minutes pass by before Arthur, with a beaming smile on his face, comes back to take his seat beside me.

"Well, what's it all about?" I enquire.

"Bingo!" says Arthur.

"What do you mean Bingo!"

"Friday night is Bingo night and they all come here for the first house of the night at 7 o'clock because it's a big jackpot!"

"Yes, I know that! I was here with you when we arrived and the place was packed and they all played Bingo!"

"Well, after that flyer they have a flyer at the Conservative Club across the road, so they all go there!"

"Have they got an artist on at that place?"

"Yes, he's just going on stage now"

"But there's nobody over there, they've all come back over here!"

"Yes, they stagger the Bingo and the artists so they don't clash"

"Correct me if I'm wrong Arthur but if that's the case, why on earth do they have an artist on at both clubs?"

"Well the Concert Chairman says that they wouldn't turn out if there wasn't an artist on!"

So I spend the rest of the night sitting in a club full of people whilst they play Bingo and sing to an empty auditorium when I'm on stage; strange world!

Thirty Seven

Leigh

Similar to Westhoughton in geography, geology (lots of mines), industry (cotton mills) and agriculture (originally a farming area), Leigh lies about twelve miles from Manchester. Railways and canals run through the town whilst seams of coal run under it. It has a few famous sons including Georgie Fame the singer and James Hilton, author of 'Goodbye Mr. Chips' was born there. During the 1960's there was a documentary shown on regional television telling of the exploits of a gang of lads from the town. Their hobby in the evenings was to go out 'lamping' for rabbits. The bright light would attract 'Bright Eyes' and there it would stand, mesmerised, whilst the lads released their Jack Russell terriers and it's rabbit pie for tea! The only reason I mention this tale is that a regional programme, made in the North West for a North West audience had subtitles! 'Leythers', as they are known locally are a different breed, different habits and have a rather quaint dialect!

I did a gig at the Plank Lane Catholic Club, otherwise known as 'Plonk Lone'. I'd been on stage a few minutes and the crowd were being reasonably civilised, when all of a sudden the Concert Secretary dashed onto the stage and snatched the microphone from my hands.

"Shut up you lot! Give this lad a chance. He's not been going long and I'm fed up with your behaviour."

The crowd who, up to now had been, I thought, relatively well behaved, were beginning to rebel. It was obvious that he disliked several members in the audience and that the feelings were mutual.

"If you lot don't shut up I'll shut the bar!"

Shut the bar! There'll be a riot if you do!

The audience were getting more and more restless and some began to throw their cardboards place mats towards the stage.

"You think I'm joking don't you – well I'm not and if you don't start behaving yourselves I'll not only shut the bar, I'll shut the bloody club!"

"Don't be bloody stupid Fred! Let the lad carry on singing!"

He'd obviously been to the Saddam Hussein school of diplomacy, although we didn't know about Saddam at the time. People were beginning to stand up and throw ash trays towards the stage. Blokes were booing and women were whistling as the audience began banging their glasses on the table tops. It appeared that we were about to re-enact the Storming of the Bastille, the stage being Paris' fortress-prison, when all of a sudden Fred loses his nerve, passes the microphone back to me with the parting shot, "Well lad, you'd better get on with it!" and he walks off stage leaving me with Santa Anna and his army about to storm the Alamo! Unfortunately, I've not got my bowie knife with me neither do I have Davie Crockett by my side!

Get on with it, you must be joking. How am I going to get through this.

Now I know what it must have felt like for Michael Caine at Rouke's Drift during the epic battle with the Zulu nation. I nearly broke into 'Men of Harlech', like Ivor Emmanuel did in the film. However, I was in Plonk Lane not Natal in South Africa, so they got 'Ten Guitars' like everybody else!

Thirty Eight

Friday Nights

It was becoming a bit of a ritual, going to the Red Lion folk club on a Friday night. I made lots of friends including a group of blokes who came all the way from Appley Bridge, the far side of Wigan. Appley Bridge probably got its' name from a large apple tree that grew next to a bridge over the River Douglas which gave access to the town. The bridge has been replaced several times over the years and one story goes that they chopped down the tree to use the wood for the new bridge. Nothing happens in the town apart from the odd meteorite shower! In October 1914, the sky lit up when a meteorite weighing 33lbs. landed in a farmer's field. The fragment was put on display in a shop window so that the whole the village (all 10 of them) could view the offending chunk!

The only other tale that I could find out about this sleepy little village was relating to Skull House Lane. During the English Civil war, Mr. Cromwell and his roundheads decided that monks and monasteries should be destroyed. To that end they went on a killing spree of anything religious. When they arrived in Appley Bridge, they heard that a monk was hiding in a house down the lane. To escape from his pursuers the man of the cloth had taken refuge up the chimney! To get him out, the roundheads lit a fire in the hearth which probably seared his cassocks! He was then dragged from the fireplace, murdered and his skull was left on the fireplace on display to any other cleric who thought they could get away from Oliver C. and his gang!

Now here comes the spooky bit; if anyone tried to remove the skull they were to come to a sticky end. Someone threw it in the River Douglas but the skull mysteriously returned to its place on the hearth and the offending person drowned several days later. Up until a few years ago, if anyone threw something in the Douglas it would probably float with all the rubbish in that particular watercourse! Anyone else who tried to get rid of the offending cranium was to meet severe misfortune, even death, so it is now left alone and the lane got its name from this unfortunate incident.

John, Frank and Ken travelled together from Appley Bridge in John's car. He was a car salesman and so would turn up in all sorts of vehicles, from battered old vans to top of the range sports cars. His favourite was a bright orange Citroen Diane, probably because he couldn't sell it! We all became close friends and would regularly meet up for a night on the town, or a visit to another folk club in the area. On one visit to the Red Lion on a Friday we were surprised to see that one of the group was missing. We were to find out later that Norman Prince had relinquished his ties with the Auld Triangle and was doing work with other bands. John suggested that we took him out for a night and so we rang him up and it was arranged that we'd have a night out at a folk club in Wigan.

In conversation during the night it came as a surprise to everyone when John announced that he'd like to be in a folk group. I, of course, loved the camaraderie of these evenings but unfortunately there was no money in it! I was beginning to earn quite a few pounds extra every week which I had come to rely on. "Anyway", I said, "none of us can play an instrument apart from me, and I don't think a badly played trombone would work in a folk band!"

"What do you mean!" cried Norman, "I play guitar!"

"Like I said, nobody amongst the three of us can play an instrument but I know someone who can!"

"Who's that?" they bark in unison.

"Well, as you know, I used to do shows down at the Youth Club and the entire band consisted of our Jimmy and David Littler. Our Jimmy's still with the Auld Triangle but maybe David would be interested in forming a group with the three of us?"

Thirty Nine

The Beginning

So arrangements are made and David agrees to meet us for a drink whilst we discuss a possible foray into the wonderful world of entertainment. It's agreed that before we make any decisions we need to get together with instruments and try to work out a song or two. Although Norman might know a few folk songs, it would be up to John and myself to sing them to an audience. David has no folk background at all and the only songs I know are the ones I've heard at the folk clubs I've attended or the ones on my only folk album, the Clancy Brothers and Tommy Makem. The upstairs room in the Red Lion is a possible venue for us to rehearse but let's not get ahead of ourselves! We don't even know if this is worth pursuing, let's try a few nights in David's kitchen!

David had just bought a house on Park Road and was in the process of doing lots of refurbishments. It would be his first home, as he and his wife had been living with the in-laws. It was therefore agreed that we could use the four bare walls to rehearse in exchange for a help with the decorating. This agreed, we got together and tried to see if, although we all knew a song or two, did we all know the same one? The answer was unfortunately no, but as I'm a quick learner, it was decided that if there was a song that I liked, I would quickly learn the words. What would we do if John liked the song as well! Then the other two would decide who sounded best when they sang it! Had we got albums with the words on?, that was always a problem; there was no Internet to research the lyrics so there were times I would learn words from an album. Sometimes I wasn't sure what was being said, so in true folk tradition, I made them up! That's why you might hear a folk song that's very old and there are loads of different words to that particular piece. I suppose it's like 'Chinese whisper', the wandering minstrel travelled from town to town singing a song that he'd just written, unfortunately he sang with a Geordie accent and the bloke from Leigh couldn't understand him so he made some verses up. When the minstrel from Leigh went on the road, nobody in the country could understand him so the words got changed again, and so on and so on!

Most of the songs told of love that's been lost, of soldiers going off to war and of drinking which are my particular favourites. They are passed down from generation to generations with new additions along the way. They come from all sources both great and small. My grandmother used to sing a song about the Boer War but I was too young, or too idle to put the words down for posterity. Cecil Sharpe, the English folklorist, travelled to the Appalachian mountains in the early 20th century, in search of old English and Scottish songs that had been passed down for generations from their original British ancestors. Bob Dylan, for example, has used several British folk tunes in his repertoire over the years.

So off we'd go with words in hand, chords in the case of David and Norman, and practice, practice, practice! Eventually we had a handful of songs that all four of us could perform together. So what next? How do we become more famous than Elvis? Is the world ready for us? First of all, it might be useful if we sang in front of an audience and see what they think. So, similar to my outings with Arthur, the four of us go on the road in search of fame. We thought it might be a good idea to do a few floor spots (auditions) in the hope of some business. At the time, money was not an issue; if we got enough to cover our expenses for the night then that's O.K. Anyway, as I'd previously stated, there's no money in folk music!

One evening, as an afterthought, one of us said, "What are we going to call the group?"

"Never thought about that came the reply!"

We then spent the next half hour thinking up the most ridiculous names imaginable. After a while we became sensible and tried to think of a name that was appropriate. We were thinking of the names of the day, Spinners, Tinkers, Beggarmen, Dubliners. Then Christine, David's wife said, "What about the Westhoughton Weavers?"

"Thanks, Christine but that's rubbish. Nobody will like that name will they?"

"Probably not!"

"Well, have a think about it because we'll need a name eventually!"

Following several more rehearsals in David's kitchen we embark on our first public outing. It was to be at the Wigan folk club which was based in the 'Riverside Club', attached to Central Park, the home of Wigan Rugby League Club. Wigan Rugby League club played their first ever match at the famous stadium on 6th September 1902 when they beat Batley 14-8. The biggest ever crowd for a league match was there when 47,747 saw Wigan beat St. Helens 19-14. The final game at rugby league's most famous arena was in September 1999 when Wigan beat their greatest ever rivals, St. Helens 28-20, a day short of ninety seven years after their first encounter against Batley. When I hear the word Central Park, all I can hear in my head is Eddie Wareing saying Centraaaal Paaark and shouting his most famous line "It's an up and under!"

Most sports stadia have a function room of sorts and this was no exception. The Riverside was known locally as a night club but on Monday nights they used a corner of it as a folk club. This is where we were about to start our careers. We arrived at approximately 7.00 p.m. to watch the resident group. I can't remember a thing about the night other than our ten minutes or so on stage. I'd been doing solo work for a year or two by this time, so I didn't particularly feel nervous. I knew they would give a reasonable amount of order and I'd been to Leigh Casino and Bamfurlong Labour Club! John and David, however, were extremely jittery but at least they had a buffer in Norman and myself. It was eventually a fairly non-event as it turned out. The only thing of note was just before we were due on stage, the organiser said, "What are you called?"

We all looked around at each other with blank faces until one of us chirped up, "We're the Westhoughton Weavers!" No-one could think of anything better and so, apart from losing a 'West', the name stuck!

There were only a handful present in the room and we only managed three songs which were received kindly. We didn't get a booking from the night but at least it was over and we'd performed! On the way home we were dissecting the performance and everyone agreed that there was potential. All we needed was a few more bookings and we'd be more confident and relaxed next time. The problem was, where do we get bookings from? There weren't any Arthur's around and most folk groups didn't have agents, not that we were on the lookout for one of those!

It was left to Norman to ring around people in the folk circles that he knew in an attempt to generate some business. Personally I'd quite enjoyed the evening because there was very little stress and the fact that there were four of us on stage seemed to dissipate the worrying aspects. The most notable thing however, was the fact that the audience sat and listened, even though they'd never heard of us before. Some even came over following our performance to congratulate us on a job well done! But it's back to work tomorrow, so we can talk about folk music another time!

Forty

Life Goes On

Life was hectic and it was a juggling act between work, leisure (not much of that!), solo singing, constantly learning songs and rehearsing with the newly formed Houghton Weavers. The one thing missing for the group was work! We'd get the very occasional gig but they were few and far between. Most folk clubs, and there were hundreds of them in the mid-seventies, had a planned yearly schedule which meant that reasonable acts were re-booked for the same time next year and any new acts had to rely on other acts disbanding or dropping dead before an opening became available. Once on the circuit, it was relatively easy to get regular gigs automatically but the question was, how do you get on the circuit? Then the solution seemed to appear out of thin air – Why not create our own circuit!

And that's exactly what we did! We formed a small folk club at the Duke of York pub in Chorley whilst on the lookout for larger and more improved venues.

Eventually, the Last Drop village in Bolton decided they'd try a regular folk night in their Drop Inn, using the Weavers as the resident act. Despite having the appearance of an actual eighteenth century village, this complex, on the outskirts of Bolton in the Bromley Cross area, is actually a collection of old houses that have been put together to form shops, a pub and a hotel. We played there on a Monday night for all the young yuppies trying to impress their girlfriends – they must have thought that we were very quaint!

Cassinelli's motel, now a Premier Inn at Almond Brook, Standish, was the scene for our second major venture. We began a regular folk night, with guests, in their function room. We booked all the acts to appear and the hotel paid us a small retainer whilst the proceeds from the entrance fee paid for the guest. The entrance fee in those days was fifty pence which included supper! They must have used the leftover food to produce such delicacies as Curried Lancashire Hotpot!

Finally, the biggest venue that we acquired during that period was at Park Hall, Charnock Richard. Home of the Camelot theme park, Park Hall sits in over 100 acres of wooded countryside and boasts a hotel, cabaret lounge and health spa. We performed every week in the medieval banqueting hall that could hold around five hundred people. We were again paid to perform by the venue and the receipts from the entrance monies was used to pay the guest. Because of the size of the venue we could attract bigger named acts, which in turn attracted bigger audiences. These weekly folk clubs spawned more work and required us to learn new material every week. A lot of the acts had their own residencies and so reciprocal bookings began, together with work offers from members of the audience and the odd agent who would come to see what all the fuss was about!

To finally top it all, we decided to open up a club in Westhoughton, at the cricket club. This was going to be our home for quite a few years and we cajoled and tempted all our friends to attend to give ourselves a semblance of popularity. We never felt that we were in opposition to The Red Lion folk club as ours attracted quite a different clientele. The Red Lion attracted 'folkies' whereas we were trying to convert people into becoming 'folkies'. We didn't mind the crowd making a bit of noise, I was used to working in Platt Bridge after all! This meant that our weekly commitment read as follows: Monday, Last Drop, Tuesday, Park Hall, Wednesday, relax or collapse, Thursday, Casinelli's, Friday, night out with the boys, Saturday, usually working with Arthur and finally, Sunday, cricket club. Not forgetting five days a week at work and the occasional booking for the Weavers!

Forty One

A Life on the Ocean Wave

One of these 'off-shoot' bookings came around this time. The organiser of a boat trip rang to see if we would be willing to entertain a party who would be spending the evening on a narrow boat. The plan would be to travel up and down the Leeds-Liverpool canal for about three hours with a break for food and as much drink as they could afford! We'd sing for an hour as the boat travelled in one direction. At a wider part of the canal the idea was to have supper whilst the boat turned round, then another hour to take us back home.

The Leeds-Liverpool canal is the longest navigation in Britain. At just over a hundred and twenty seven miles, with ninety one locks, it links the seaport of Liverpool with the Calder Navigation at Leeds, which in turn can form a through route from the Irish to the North Sea. So, should we ever decide to become independent from the 'southern jessies', then we already have a ready-made boundary! Notable features on the canal include the route through Aintree giving rise to the 'Canal Turn' on the famous Grand National course. It passes the notorious Wigan Pier, made famous by George Formby senior and then goes into the hills of Lancashire, where it enters the 'mile tunnel' at Foulridge on the Lancashire/Yorkshire border. In 1796, after five years of excavating, the mile tunnel was opened. Because the tunnel was so long and there's no towpath for a horse, the bargee had to push his craft through the subway by means of 'walking' along the ceiling – this was referred to as 'legging it'. Thieves now use that expression when confronted by an officer of the law! There's also a tale about a cow that fell in the 'cut' at the tunnel's entrance and swam the whole mile before being rescued at the other end!

So we arrive at the pub in Burscough, where the trip will set sail. First problem was electricity; it was either play totally unaccompanied or start up a petrol generator to give us power. The argument was, they might not be a 'folky' crowd who would stay quiet and listen, which meant no electricity needed; or, they could be quite noisy so we'd need to amplify things. The decision was to amplify things just in case and if they kept quiet we could switch it off.

That duly decided, we tried to start up the generator which was clunking and banging until it eventually fired into life. Once the choke was no longer needed it continued, not to necessarily 'purr', but to 'growl'. The generator was then placed outside, above the entrance to the cabin (where Rosie and Jim usually sit!) and we worked below. At the bottom of the steps we set up our

223

microphones and amps in preparation for the audience. Unfortunately, this was the only means of access to the rest of the vessel so when people arrived, they were kicking over stands and guitars; and all this before they'd had a drink! Eventually everyone arrived and began jostling for position. To our left was the bar which was doing a roaring trade. Next door to the bar, which was a tiny hatch cut in a small cupboard, was the only toilet on board. So, throughout the evening everyone had to push past me to access the lavatory, or should I say bucket! It was necessary to turn our volume up to full throttle, not only because of the noise from the generator but because the audience were beginning to get quite lively. Apart from that though, everything seemed to be going quite well.

We'd done about an hour on stage when the boat slowly pulled into a mooring. The lady organiser enquired if we'd like some supper with the rest of them. When we answered in the affirmative her assistant left the boat to go to the local 'chippy'. She returned with fish and chips for 40 or so people shortly afterwards. We then continued on our journey back to Burscough, us singing, them supping! People emerging from the toilet were becoming more and more perplexed as the bucket was getting perilously close to overflowing! Eventually, our captain came to the rescue; walking into the closet, emerging, with bucket in hand and promptly emptying its contents overboard into the canal – no wonder there's not many fish around there!

On arrival back at the pub, everyone appeared to have had a good time, although the main topic of conversation seemed to be regarding the latrine! The lady organiser took us to one side and pronounced that all had had a great night. "Now", she continued, "the fee for the evening was £15, fine! How many fish and chips did you have?" And I will never forget until my dying day; she subtracted the cost of fish and chips from the £15 and gave us a cheque for the remainder!"

What good is a bloody cheque! I can't buy beer with a cheque! We're going to have to open a bank account. How many fish and chips!

Forty Two

Mid 70's

This period saw the birth of modern computing with very basic personal computers and pocket calculators, together with floppy disks and the emergence of fibre optics. Women were taking over the world; I've already mentioned 'Maggie' becoming leader of the Tories, Isabel Peron became President of Argentina (She's not 'Evita', that was Peron's second wife whilst Isabel was his third one!); Indira Gandhi remains Prime Minister of India; Golda Meir remains in charge of Israel and even the Peoples republic of China opt for a female Chairman (or chairwoman in this case) in Soon Ching-ling! 'One Flew over the Cuckoo's Nest' won the Oscar for best film in 1975 and the following year it was won by 'Rocky'. Fawlty Towers first appeared on telly in 1975 and the following year Bill Grundy was temporarily sacked following an interview with the Sex Pistols when he appeared to goad them into obscenities before the watershed. The only thing we had in common with the

Sex Pistols was that we both did our first recording in 1976! Their's was a single titled 'Anarchy in the UK', and reached number thirty eight in the singles charts. It was to be the only recording that EMI issued as the group were dropped by the company following that Bill Grundy incident.

We'd been singing around the area for about a year and it was suggested that we record an album. It was about this time that we were joined on stage by David's brother, Denis. He was a reasonably proficient bass guitar player and we started to use him more often, to 'beef up' our sound. He had practiced with us for a while and slowly became a member of the group without anybody realising it. We talked to various people 'in the know' in the hope of getting someone to record us. There didn't appear to be much expectation, until one day, a well known folk singer, Brian Dewhurst, rang us to say that a record company was willing to take a gamble on us, on his endorsement. Needless to say, we were over the moon to be actually going into a proper studio to record a proper record for a proper company. Arrangements were made to keep a weekend free in all of our diaries to travel to the Folk Heritage recording studios in Llanfair Caereinion (try saying that when you've had a few!)

Alan Green, the proprietor of Folk Heritage had reached an agreement with Brian, to allow a trainee recording engineer to use his facilities for a few days. It would give him a chance to get used to his recording studio whilst getting a troublesome group (us) off his back! We, of course, didn't know this and were buoyed with enthusiasm as the recording 'D-day' approached.

We told everybody about our impending good fortune and it was suggested that we contact the local newspapers to see if they would be interested in writing an article in their broadsheet. The Bolton Evening News replied to say they would certainly do a feature but would require a photograph for publication. No problem at all! It was arranged to do the photograph on Tuesday night on the streets of Westhoughton, so all members were contacted. Unfortunately, John said he was unable to attend as he had something else booked. When pressed on the matter he admitted that he was going out for a pint with his mates.

"But John", we said, "this is so important. Surely you can go out with your mates another night!"

"No, I've made arrangements and there's nothing I can do about it!"

"Of course there's something you can do about it, just cancel it!"

"No chance! I'd rather go out with my mates anyway!"

The conversation then developed into an argument which eventually became so heated that it ended with this ultimatum.

"Well, if you can't be bothered to turn up for a very important photo shoot then we can't be bothered having you in the group! Turn up on Tuesday or you're out!"

So Tuesday arrived but John didn't and we reluctantly had to continue without him.

From that point onwards we went through a manic few days. We were due to do this recording and we'd spent several weeks rehearsing for it but that was with five of us not four! We therefore had to try to rearrange all the pieces so that they would be equally balanced musically and the songs that John was going to sing had to be replaced by others. This was so important, we couldn't cancel, we had to get it right, so we rehearsed and rehearsed until the time to go to welsh Wales!

Forty Three

Bookings Still Coming In

We were getting quite a few more bookings now. One I particularly remember was in a little village hall on the outskirts of Wigan. Everything was going smoothly and we were just nearing the end of our first half. The lady organiser had asked us to announce the last song so that supper could be prepared for serving. Not a problem, we were at that point of the night and an announcement to that effect was made. At the end of the song, we were about to walk off the stage when the same lady appeared at the kitchen door and asked if it would be possible to sing another song. "That's fine!", we declared and sang another number. Once again, at the end of the song the woman appeared at the door to ask if we could continue for one more song. This went on a further two songs until we'd had enough of it.

"We can do as long as you want! We can sing for an hour or for two hours but why do you keep asking us to do one more song, then another and so on?"

"Well you see", came the reply, "We're having potato pie for supper and we're cooking it in the kitchen".

"Yes! So what's the problem?"

"Well, the potato pie has a crust and it's still not cooked, so I'd be most grateful if you sang just one more!"

Forty Four

Ruthin

Around this time we actually got a booking in Wales, at Ruthin (pronounced Rithin) rugby club. An extremely long distance gig for us at the time but we approached it with enthusiasm. Leaving work early on the Friday night we drove down to North Wales. When I said we drove, I didn't actually drive at the time, so I was taxied by one of the other members. In those days, on such a long journey, we'd travel in one car with just a couple of guitars in the boot. On stage, we wore what we arrived in, no posh costume changes for the lads from Westhoughton! On arrival in the town? village? hamlet? three houses and a pub, we looked around to see if anybody could tell us where the rugby club was. Friday night and not a soul to be seen, really buzzing in Ruthin tonight. Eventually, in the distance, we spotted a policeman on his bike. We drove slowly through the place and pulled up alongside him and his bike.

"Excuse me please, do you know the way to the rugby club?"

"Oh, I'm sorry, I don't. I'm from the next village and I'm only here for the day to help them out!"

So much for the saying, 'ask a policeman!'

Which reminds me of the vicar who lived in a small place like Ruthin. His house was next door to the church and every morning he would go to his shed, climb on his bike and peddle down the hill to visit his parishioners. In the village lived a policeman who utterly adored his job. He liked nothing more than booking people and was proud of the fact that everyone in the village had been booked for some misdemeanour or other. That is, except the vicar who lived on the top of the hill. One night, the constable walked up to the vicar's house, went round the back, into the shed and removed the brake blocks from the vicar's bicycle.

The following morning, the officer, attired in his newly cleaned uniform, was waiting at the bottom of the hill with notepad in hand and pencil newly sharpened. As the vicar began to speed down the incline, the bobby slowly emerged from behind a parked van and shouted "Halt!"

Amazingly, the bike screeched to a halt in front of the patrolman, who bemusedly announced, "How on earth did you do that? You know I've booked everyone in this town except you. I even came up to your house last night and took the brake pads off your bike so that you wouldn't be able to stop!"

The vicar smiled and said, "My son, when I ride this bike the Lord rides with me!"

"Got you at last, cries the policeman! You're booked...TWO on a bike!"

Back to our story, we go round a few more bends and there it is! Ruthin Rugby Club! Unfortunately it appears as busy as the town. Not a sign of anybody, so we sit in the car, twiddling our thumbs.

"Are you sure we've got the right night?"

"Is this the place, or is there another rugby club round here?"

After what seems like an eternity, we spot a bloke turning the corner and going round the back of the building. Eventually, a light flickers on to illuminate the entrance. As we stroll across the car park and enter the hall there's a bloke rearranging seats to accommodate what we hope will be a great crowd, He's setting up a table at the back to collect tickets and money and everything has just started to brighten up.

"Hello, we are the group, I'm Tony etc. etc.."

"Hi, I'm the organiser of the folk club. We've had a bit of a problem, I think I'd better explain. Last week was the last folk night before the summer break. I'd forgotten that I'd booked you so nobody knows you're coming but maybe one or two will turn up if we're lucky!"

Great! So much for our International outing! So what do we do now?

"If you'd like to wait for half an hour, just in case somebody turns up?"

So we wait, and we wait and eventually we decide that this outing was a bit of a disaster. How can we cheer ourselves up? Let's have a Friday night out in Ruthin! We leave the club with a few quid from the organiser, just to cover some expenses and make our way into the metropolis! One of John Denver's songs springs to mind.......

Saturday night in Toledo, Ohio, is like being nowhere at all.....

Well I know a town that Toledo could twin with!

Forty Five

Scotland

Around this time we were fortunate enough to be invited to another foreign country! Some friends of ours, Jacqui and Bridie, a folk duo from Liverpool, who were the funniest female outfit on the folk circuit, come to think of it, they were the only female duo on the folk circuit, were responsible for booking acts into two Scottish restaurants. McTavish's Kitchen was the name of two restaurants that catered for the influx of tourists to the Scottish Highlands. There was one in Oban and the other, further north, in Fort William. The restaurants had a Highland dancer as their resident act, together with a Highland piper, who were joined each week with a guest folk act. We, as the guest folk act, were to spend a whole week in Fort William in the summer of 1976 and the following year we visited Oban. Accommodation was provided, as was a few pounds for spending money. You wouldn't get rich there but if you combined the evening work with a holiday then it was great. We were to perform for seven nights for approximately an hour each night.

It was quite exciting and our first trip that required us to stay away from home. We'd all taken a week off work and were immensely looking forward to the escapade! We'd estimated that the journey would take approximately six hours but it was more like nine! The roads in Scotland weren't very good in those days and if you got stuck behind a juggernaut you were in for an extended journey! The greatest thing that struck me during the long ride was when we entered the valley of Glencoe. As you drive through this awe-inspiring valley you can feel the spectacular mountains overpowering you with their grandeur. The dramatic waterfalls add to the splendour of a gorge that was created some 400 million years before, following the eruption of a super volcano and was further shaped some 10,000 years ago by the last ice age.

Many people talk about the majesty of this valley but most only talk about the Massacre of Glencoe that took place in 1692. From 1501, following the capture of a Campbell castle by a MacDonald raiding party, the two clans were at loggerheads for almost 200 years. Many atrocities happened during those two centuries and many, many people were killed from both sides of the divide.

In early 1691, King William of Orange offered a pardon to all the clans who fought against him during the Jacobite uprising of 1689. The pardon was conditional on the leaders of each clan taking an oath of allegiance before the start of the New Year. The clan Chief Alastair

MacDonald, leaving it a bit late, arrived in Inverlochy (now Fort William) on the last day of 1691, to be told he should have been in Inverary instead! When he got there he was 5 days late and his name didn't appear on any list of clans who had signed allegiance. The Secretary of State for Scotland wanted to make an example of one of the clans, to bring them into line, so the MacDonalds were chosen, as they were not particulary liked and were known as horse thieves and vagabonds.

During the month of January, 130 troops were billeted with the MacDonalds in the valley of Glencoe. They were commanded by a Captain Robert Campbell who had written orders to.....*"fall upon the rebels and put all to the sword under 70."*

So, at 5.00 a.m. on the 13th February 1692, thirty eight members of the MacDonald clan were slaughtered and many more died of exposure in the surrounding mountains. Of the 130 troops who attacked that morning, only twelve were members of the Campbell clan and their orders came from much higher up than them. It was better for the Government to blame the attack on the clan's fiercest rivals than to take responsibility themselves but from that moment onwards the undying motto of any MacDonald is, 'Never trust a Campbell!'

Because of the delay in getting to the venue, we arrived for our first night at the very last minute, so before we went on stage we all ordered a Glencoe whisky, which is like firewater! Everyone had a sip and gasped so it was up to me to keep up our image so I drained all four glasses! Within a couple of minutes on stage I was feeling quite tipsy, when I heard, "Neaw, what's gooin' on here! We travel 200 miles and still can't get away from you!" and into the restaurant walked a dozen blokes from Westhoughton. They were all members of the Rotary Club and were spending a night in Fort William before attempting the Three Peaks Challenge. This is a gruelling event where people attempt to scale the highest mountains of Scotland, England and Wales. Starting at Ben Nevis they go up and down the mountain, travel by road, whilst adhering to speed restrictions, up and down Scafell Pike in the Lake District and finally, Snowdon in Wales, all within 24 hours! I knew some of the participants vaguely but we developed a friendship, not only with the blokes but with Rotary itself following that evening, that has lasted to this day. Apparently, they broke the civilian record at the time by several hours – Tough these Westhoughton folk!

During the day, we had a few drives out to see the incredibly beautiful scenery that Scotland has to offer. As we were so close, we just had to go and find the Loch Ness monster! We drove in David's mini to the awesome stretch of water that is 21.8 square miles and is 755 feet deep in places. It holds more water than all the lakes in England and Wales put together! So where will we find 'Nessie'? Castle Urquhart seemed a reasonable place to start. It stands on the north shore of the lake and overlooks vast tracts of the loch. There's been a castle there since 1200 A.D. but there are signs that there was a fortress during the Iron Age.

The day was quite cold so I decided to stay 'indoors'. Sitting in the passenger seat an idea sprung in my little warped mind. *If we can't see Nessie then we could probably 'create' him!*

"David, have you got that marker pen?"

"Yeah, why?"

"Well, if you drew Nessie on the windscreen of your car and then took a photograph from inside, it might look like the drawing is actually the monster!"

So we tried it, David put a blob of ink on the car window. Looking through the viewfinder of my camera it looked too large to give the impression of the 'beastie'.

"David, it's too big! Can you rub a bit of it out so that it looks smaller?"

That done, I looked through the camera again and lo and behold!, it really gave an impression that there was something in the water! And the smudge made by David's finger to rub it out looked like the 'wake' created by the creature as it surfaced. That was the end of that! Totally forgotten until I had the photographs developed on arrival home. David, at the time, worked for the Bolton Evening News and when he saw the resultant photograph he asked if he could borrow it. Later that day he rang to say that the editor of the newspaper believed that he had in his possession, an image of the most sought after beast in the world! He was about to 'stop the press' and stick our picture on the front page when David chickened out and admitted that it was a hoax. We did manage to get the picture in the Evening

News but it was relegated to page 5, with the headline 'What a Whopper', together with an explanation of how it was conceived!

Forty Six

Recording

Our next visit to Wales was to be the zenith of our exploits to date. We were at last going to record an album that could potentially rival Elvis or the Beatles for worldwide sales. Westhoughton would become a place of pilgrimage like Penny Lane and Gracelands. They would sell matching David and Denis Littler bedside lamps, Norman Prince embroidered cardigans and Tony Berry blow up dolls! There would be replicas of us all in every Madame Tussauds in the world. We'd probably be made knights of the realm and be invited to join the Queen at Buckingham palace for lunch and have dinner with the P.M. Then again, we might not!

It was agreed that we'd take the Friday off work and drive down early enough to spend some hours in the studio, then we could use all day Saturday and Sunday to finish it off. That seems an inordinately long time to record a dozen songs that would only last about 45 minutes when completed but I really didn't know the protocol entailed on such an assignment.

We'd had our photos taken and our faces had been emblazoned across the Bolton Evening News telling the world that we were about to 'cut a disc' (let's use the right phraseology now that were soon to become recording artists). We counted the days and minutes until we could say goodbye to England and travel to a strange land to 'lay down some tracks'. We would be staying at a small bed and breakfast in the village, so we checked in there and asked for directions to the studio. We followed them, out of town through the rambling hills of Mid Wales, across some very dodgy dirt tracks, up another hill, round a bend and there in front of us was.......a ruined building! It was actually an old farmhouse that we realised was being renovated when we got a bit nearer. There would be no external noises to worry about in the recording studio up here, if you can discount the sheep! We were miles from anywhere and we'd yet to see a soul. We eventually arrived on the driveway in front of the building and there, sitting on a bench, rolling a cigarette was a thick set bloke of about 5'10", straggly blonde thinning hair, in jeans and a ragged tee shirt. He motioned us over to join him which we readily did.

In very gentle and hushed tones he utters, "Hi, my name's Alan Green. I assume you're the Houghton Weavers?"

This was our first introductions to a man who became a dear friend and an integral part of our later successes. We were to find out that he was from

Lancashire and had moved to Wales to expand his recording business.

"I'll give you a guided tour lads! Follow me!"

There was a working kitchen with electricity and water though little else. Pride of place was his 24 channel recording desk which was around six feet deep and at least 10 feet long.

"How on earth did you get that in here?"

"Oh, I didn't, we brought the desk up here, placed it in position and built the room round it! There was no need to hide it whilst we were building. First of all nobody knows that there's a studio up here and if they did how would they steal something that big!"

The only other habitable room was where we would spend the next few days, the recording studio itself. There were microphones, stands and leads everywhere.

I just hope we can do it all justice!

"So, who's the lad who's going to record us?" someone chirped.

"Now that's a bit of a problem!" replied Alan, "he came in last week but I haven't seen him since"

"So where is he?"

244

"Don't know! I think he realised that it wasn't the thing for him so he's gone!"

Oh, no! All our dreams shattered in an instant!

"So does that mean we might as well go home?"

"Don't worry lads, a promise is a promise and I **promised** Brian Dewhurst that this studio would record you. You'll just have to put up with me!"

So, for the rest of the weekend we all got to know each other and spent an enjoyable, though intense time recording our first real album. It's quite different to what you'd expect. It's built up like a wall. You start with the foundations and add more and more things until you get a finished product. When you hear the term 8 or 24 track studio it means that you can put down 8 or twenty four 'layers' of music. A basic sound for a group like ourselves would mean recording bass and guitar with a 'guide' vocal track to keep it all together. You can then add another guitar track, a banjo track, mouth organ, violin, piano and so on. Every one of these tracks can be re-done without altering the others. When you're happy with all that, you'd probably then add a lead vocal and maybe some backing vocals. If you need the song to sound raucous you can add three voices together on a track, then add the same three vocals on the next track so you can finish up with the sound of a choir if required. Some studios use 48 tracks or more which is incredible when you consider that arguably one of the greatest pop albums of all time 'St. Pepper's Lonely Hearts Club Band' used only four tracks!

Once you've recorded all these instruments and voices it's then time to 'mix' the finished article. Maybe the guitar track should be louder, maybe the piano needs to go down in volume, what about some reverb on the vocals, etc. All this needs either a committee, to decide on a finished product which could take weeks, or it's left to the experts in the studio, with maybe an odd comment if a particular point of view is to be taken into account. Once you've done all that, a quarter inch tape is created which will then be 'mastered' and sent to the 'pressing plant' where the actual L.P.'s are produced. So now, off you go and make an album yourself!

Alan lived in the village at the bottom of the hill, near the bed and breakfast, approximately equidistant from the pub. We'd meet up there after work and discuss how the day had gone. Generally, Alan was happy with our performance and said that once the finished product was available, he'd delivery it to the 'far north' and we could buy him a drink! His main financial concern was the number of records we could sell. He concurred that if we could flog 500 albums he would happily record us again!

Once that was agreed we began to talk about his business and artists that he had recorded. He went on to tell us about a group that had been in the studio the previous week.

"I'd recorded this fiddle player but when it was played back we could hear a banging noise. Eventually we all realised that the fiddler was tapping his feet whilst playing! The bloke says to me, 'But I can't play unless I tap my feet!' OK! I say, but we'll need to put something under your foot so that we can't hear it!"

We find a cushion and place it under the guy's foot and re-record it all again. We play it back and the noise is still there. I ask another member of the group to go into the studio with him to see if they can find where the noise is coming from. He comes out several minutes later with a smile on his face. "Do you know that pillow that you put under his right foot? Well, he's now tapping his left foot!"

"Bloody fiddlers, they're all the same", Alan retorts!

"What's the difference between a fiddle and a violin? Nobody minds if you spill beer on a fiddle! What's the difference between a fiddle and a cello? A cello burns longer!"

And so it went on for the rest of the weekend. Lots of camaraderie and with any luck a decent record!

Forty Seven

Solo Singing

Solo work was definitely taking a back seat by this time and Arthur realised that I was enjoying the group work far more than when I was alone on stage, so he didn't pressurise me at all. There were brief respites from the loneliness of these solo gigs, when mates came along to support me. As I'd said previously, I was a friend of Arthur's son and occasionally Kevin and sometimes other mates came along to give me support. One such night we were in Atherton, I think, and we'd decided we'd join in the evenings' entertainment by having a game of Bingo. Four of us were sat around the table reserved for the artist, playing Bingo. Fortunately, or unfortunately as the case may be, someone on our table won every single game of Bingo played that night! First time it was OK but as the night went on and we kept winning the audience started complaining, "He shouldn't be allowed to play bloody Bingo! Don't pay him, he's won enough!" If it was up to me, I'd give the money back but it wasn't me who was winning but Kevin,

Arthur and Harry, not that the audience were bothered –
it was my table therefore it was me who was winning!
When I went on stage it was totally unimportant whether
I was a decent artist or not, I had won their money,
therefore I was the enemy! They barracked me all night
which my friends thought was highly amusing.

I was becoming more and more disillusioned with
the whole rigmarole that went with my solo work. Why
put myself through hell when the group work is so
pleasant and enjoyable. I still enjoyed singing though,
even to a baying horde of inebriated Athertonians who
didn't like someone winning their Bingo prizes! The fact
was, I liked the type of material I was singing at the time
and it was certainly not acceptable in a folk club. I was
becoming more relaxed and able to deal with a
troublesome crowd but why should I have to 'deal' with a
mob when, in a folk setting, they listen and appreciate
what you're trying to do. At the moment it's possible to
combine the two. The problems will occur when I have to
decide which gig to do if two clash, although I don't
think that's going to be a problem, unless the solo gig
pays lots of dosh!

I still did the intermittent talent contest. There was
a TV show at the time called 'New Faces' which was
similar to 'Opportunity Knocks' but this show had a
panel of judges, as opposed to the general public voting
system used in 'Op Knocks' as it was known. They had
two judges who were less sympathetic than the rest, Tony
Hatch and Mickie Most; in lots of peoples' eyes they
were downright rude to the contestants, in one case
giving zero points to an unfortunate participant. The

reason that I mention all this is because they were advertising for the new series and asked if people would ring this particular number so that recruits could be sifted through in the hope of finding a new star. Arthur duly rang the number and a few days later received an invitation for us to go to the Wigan Casino, on such and such a date at such and such a time when auditions would be held. We thought it might be the breakthrough we were hoping for, so on the allotted day we arrived for interview and audition.

The place was in darkness when we arrived although the doors were all open. We walked into the theatre to be greeted by absolute silence! There wasn't a soul in sight, no instruments or piano for a band, no table and chairs for the panel who were going to grill me, not even a caretaker sweeping the floor, nothing at all! So we went home!

Forty Eight

Howfen Wakes

Howfen, is the name used by inhabitants of Westhoughton for their home town and every year, around the end of August, beginning of September, the mills used to shut down for the 'wakes' holidays. My mother taught me a song about this celebration and not only did we perform it on our first L.P. but we decided to use it as the title track. By now, we were beginning to attract quite large crowds in our four residencies and so when the album was released, we had no difficulty selling the required five hundred that Alan Green had suggested. Everything was looking up and we sent copies to all the local radio stations, in the hope that we might get the occasional track played.

Everywhere we went it was necessary to take a box or two of the new album because everybody seemed to be clamouring for a copy. We even asked a couple of girls who had become regular attendees to sell them for us.

"You can come to see the show for nothing if you'd just spend a few minutes selling records!"

So Sue and Jean began to organise the selling of merchandise and would you believe it, they're still doing it!

We were becoming quite iconic in our small town and our families would regularly turn up at gigs. David and Denis's mother, Gladys, would come to the cricket club almost every week. Together with my mother, they would quietly proclaim, with pride in their voices "They're our sons you know!"

Gladys even declared, "You're brilliant you know! I'm going to write to the BBC and tell 'em. They should have a group like you on telly! You don't believe me but I will, you'll see!"

"Thanks Gladys but they won't be interested in us!"

"You'll see, I will!"

Forty Nine

We'll Call You

In the mid 70's Regional television was quite a powerful tool and attracted massive audiences. Not forgetting that at that time, the viewing public had a choice of only three programmes as opposed to the hundreds that are now available. BBC 1 and BBC 2 had only Granada TV as competition in the North West and so to get on one of these channels was so difficult.

There was a programme on BBC1 North West, hosted by that perennial favourite, Stuart Hall. The show was called 'We'll Call You' and featured acts from around the area who were looking to be 'discovered'. Theatrical agents were forever knocking on the door of the Television Studio in the hope of getting publicity for their acts. The show was similar in concept to the massive 'Opportunity Knocks' or in today's speak, 'The X Factor', however, there was one slight difference with this particular programme in that the audience were not required to vote. There was no golden prize at the end of the journey, just a chance to be seen on TV by the whole of the North West regional audience. It was an authentic variety show with singers, comedians, groups, magicians and the like.

The show was quite popular, as Stuart Hall brought his infectious manner to our screens. He was the type of person who made you smile when you glimpsed his 'cheeky' face and one couldn't help but join in when he broke into laughter which seemed to be contagious! Stuart joined the BBC in 1959 as a general reporter. He worked his way up until he became presenter of the North West news programme between 1965 and 1990. He was to become well known nationally as a presenter of 'It's a Knockout!' and it's European equivalent 'Jeux Sans Frontière' between 1971 and 1982 and is still a football reporter for BBC Radio 5 Live where he prefers to follow his beloved Manchester City.

Unbeknown to us, Gladys had been true to her word and had written to the BBC. We didn't know this until one day we got a phone call.....

"Hello, my name's Terry Wheeler and I'm the producer of 'We'll call You!' I don't know if you know but one of the mother's of the group has written to me. I'm quite interested in coming to see you. Have you got a list of available dates please?"

Panic stations! Is this a joke? It doesn't seem like it but we have quite a few mates who would love a wind up like this.

"Well yes! but how do we know it's you?"

"Because it is me!"

"Yeah but do we know it's really you!"

"Because I've said it is! Would you like me to hang up?"

"Oh, please don't do that! I'll get my diary and give you the gigs we've got in the next few weeks"

So, it's agreed that this bloke is who he says he is and that he's going to come and watch us.

Preparations are made for Terry to come and watch us at a venue in Wigan. Now for the last thirty five years I have always thought that venue was St. Cecilia's in Wigan but I thought I'd better make sure. According to the Anglican and the Catholic diocesan almanacs there is no church of that name in Wigan or its' surrounding districts. There is, however a St. Cecelia's in Huyton but it wasn't there and there is a St. Cecelia's in Longridge......it could have been there. I always thought it was near Wigan so Longridge could be the culprit as my map reading skills leave something to be desired! So Terry Wheeler did make arrangements to come and see us but for the life of me I don't know where!

What material should we use for the night? What gags should Norman tell? What should we wear? We churned all these things around for days on end. If he likes us we could become television superstars! If he doesn't like us we've still got a decent following and we're almost ready to record a second album, so it's really a win, win situation! However, it would be much better if he did like us and gave us a chance to sing one song on TV!

As the day approached, we became more and more nervous! We kept ringing each other to change the material we were doing in the show, in the hope that the new way would be better! It was finally decided that whatever we were doing at the time tended to work with an audience, so why change if it's not broken! We tried to keep all this away from our regular audiences so that they wouldn't add to the tension or, if things didn't work out the way we'd like, to have egg on our faces. Unfortunately, our mothers told everybody that they knew, plus many that they didn't know, that their sons would be appearing on television following the visit of BBC's top man in Manchester!

Apprehension, stress and anxiety become the order of the day and all this culminated on the day of the show. We arrived at the venue to set up our sound system. We'd never been to the club before and so the siting of the speakers was of paramount importance. The stage jutted out into the auditorium so we finished up with the speakers behind the microphones, which could lead to problems later! The audience slowly made their way in but they didn't seem like a folk club audience.......we could have some trouble with this lot! It didn't help that they had a game of Bingo to start the evening ......*but don't worry, we'll sort them out, it's going to be a great night! I wonder whether he'll come and say hello, or just watch quietly in the corner. Will he come alone or might he bring other producers with him! Tony, Tony, stop worrying and try to relax! What will be, will be!*

So, eventually it was time to entertain. We duly arrived on stage and I had flashbacks of my night in Bamfurlong! Both the Littler brothers got on with their jobs but I could see that they were both petrified. Norman fluffed a gag or two and I didn't sing particularly well. Added to all that, we were getting feedback from the speakers because of their positioning and the audience must have been airlifted from Platt Wazz (the friendly term for Platt Bridge). It was terrible! We came off at half time and were in total agreement.....*I hope to god he didn't see that!* Let's hope it improves somewhat in the second half!

Well it didn't! If anything, it got worse.......the audience started talking during the songs and we were somehow gripped by an unseen force that caused us to utter total garbage at every turn. The music was poor and gradually got worse, the gags were either not understood or told particulary badly, the feedback noise from the speakers intensified and we all wished we could dig a hole and hide in it!

It probably wasn't as bad as we thought but we had built our dreams and ambitions to such a degree that anything short of perfection would not be accepted. Well, this was anything but perfection and as the evening eventually came to an end, we slunk off stage in a state of deep depression. We started by blaming the sound, then we decided it was the audience's fault but eventually we had to conclude that it was totally our responsibility and we had failed miserably!

"Let's not get too downbeat, there will be other nights when we will shine."

"That's all well and good!" one of us proclaimed, "but it was tonight that we were meant to shine!"

"Anyway, has anybody seen him?" asked David.

"No, he probably left early because it was a disaster!" replied Denis

"We could try ringing him and try and talk our way out of it?" I said in desperation.

"We don't usually have nights like that!"

"We've never had a night like that! It was a total shambles but it wasn't anybody's fault. It was just one of those nights!"

"Well I hope we don't get many more like that 'cos I'll go back to singing on my own. On second thoughts, that would have been a great night if I'd have been on my own!"

Different nights, different expectations. This night, however, had been the poorest one so far, on a night when we wanted the best so far! *Can't do anything about it now......it's passed!.....there'll always be another day.....we hope! What a missed opportunity!*

We slowly packed our things away, loaded the cars and made our weary way home. When I arrived back in Westhoughton, my mother had stayed up to see how we'd gone on. I went through the night and explained all that had happened. My mother, in her usual way told me that if that was how things were meant to happen, that there's no use crying over spilled milk. I had trouble getting to sleep, which isn't normally a problem for me. Events of the day just kept whirring around in my mind and thoughts of what might have been.

The next morning I felt just as miserable. Things were bound to get better but at the time it didn't seem like they could. We picked a really dreadful night to give our worst display so far. I know it's all down to nerves but that's no consolation whatsoever.

I was on my third cup of tea, still feeling ghastly when the phone rang and a relatively cheerful voice said, "Hi, it's Terry Wheeler from the BBC.....sorry I couldn't make it last night, can we arrange for me to come and see you again?"

But that's another story!

Other titles that you may enjoy reading from
Peak Publish

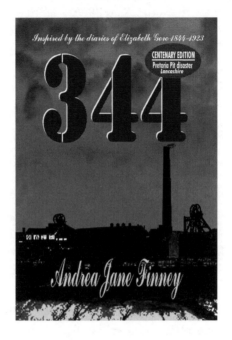

344 A story of the
Pretoria Pit Disaster
Inspired by a Mother's Tale
by
Andrea Jane Finney
ISBN: 978-1-907219-00-9

This is a story woven around the Pretoria Pit
Disaster, the third largest mining disaster in British
history inspired by Elizabeth Gore's diary (Andrea's
great, great grandmother) who lost her son in the
disaster. Andrea has also made use of the
extensive newspaper coverage reported in the
'Bolton News' at the time. Author lives in
Westhoughton, Lancashire.

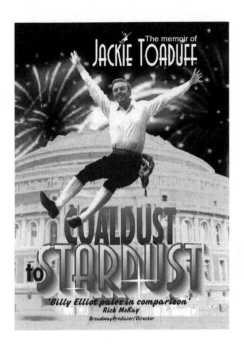

Coaldust to Stardust
by Jackie Toaduff
Billy Elliot Pales in comparison
ISBN: 978-1-907219-08-5 (Hbk)
978-1-907219-14-6 (Pbk)

The memoir of Jackie Toaduff is a heart warming story about a boys dreams becoming reality through hard work, determination and a passion for singing, dancing and entertaining and against his parents wishes as a child. A true story of a boy working for 13 years as a coal miner whilst clog dancing every chance he could. Author lives in Dronfield, Derbyshire.

KING WELFARE

...I hear you knocking

Martin Weinbren

King Welfare
by Martin Weinbren

ISBN: 978-1-907219-184

Jake Atkinson is King Welfare. That's King as in - if it's 'king welfare, tell 'em to sod off". Jake is a social worker at a local council in the East Midlands. Based on Martin Weinbren's own experience and knowledge as a social worker in various parts of the United Kingdom, King Welfare gives a gritty and gripping no-holds-barred insight into a hidden world. Published November 2010

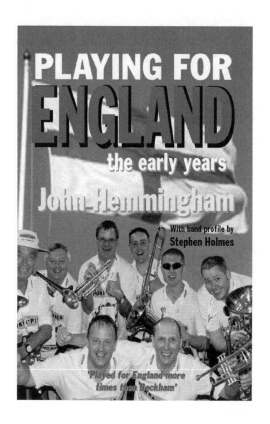

Playing for England
by John Hemmingham
ISBN: 978-1-907219-108

In the spirit of 'Fever Pitch', 'The Full
Monty' and 'Brassed Off' this is the
story of the Sheffield based England
Band supporting the England Team
since 1996 and have now have
'Played for England' more times than
Beckham'.

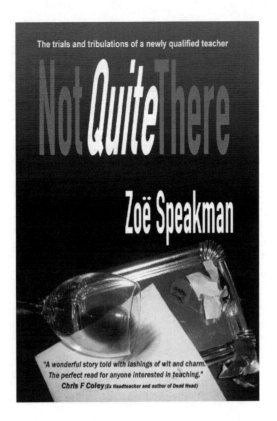

The trials and tribulations of a newly qualified teacher

Not Quite There

Zoë Speakman

"A wonderful story told with lashings of wit and charm.
The perfect read for anyone interested in teaching."
Chris F Coley (Ex Headteacher and author of Dead Head)

Not Quite There
Zoë Speakman
ISBN: 978-1-907219-214

Being a newly qualified teacher is not quite all it's cracked up to be...Emily Greenhowe, bright, new, shining NQT, stalks through the doors of Marsh View Primary School, recycled A4 pad tucked neatly under her arm, only to find that the life of a newly qualified teacher isn't as straightforward as she'd been led to believe. This is a Jumping Fish title, fiction based on fact. The author, who was a victim of bullying in her first teaching post was called to the House of Lords in 2009 to speak about bullying in the workplace. Published November 2010